THE CHILD SPEAKS

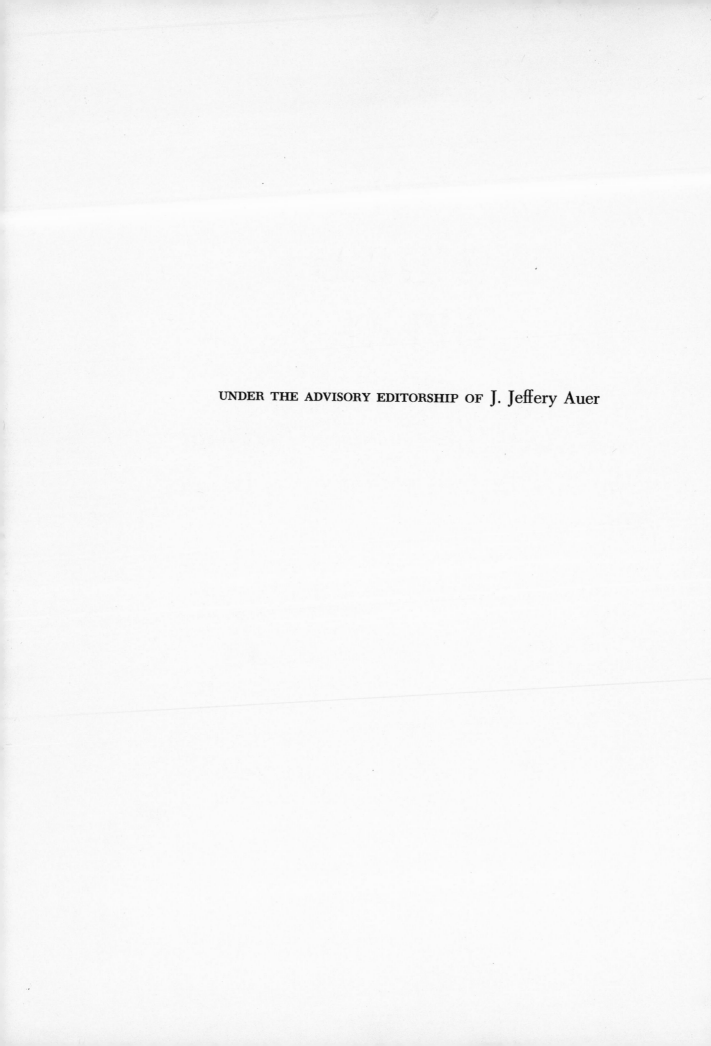

UNDER THE ADVISORY EDITORSHIP OF J. Jeffery Auer

THE CHILD SPEAKS

A Speech Improvement Program for Kindergarten and First Grade

MARGARET C. BYRNE, PH.D.

Director, Speech and Hearing Clinic
University of Kansas

HARPER & ROW, PUBLISHERS
NEW YORK, EVANSTON, AND LONDON

THE CHILD SPEAKS
A Speech Improvement Program for Kindergarten and First Grade
Copyright © 1965 by Margaret C. Byrne

LIBRARY OF CONGRESS CATALOG CARD NUMBER: 65–10417

L-O

To children everywhere who must learn the process of
oral communication—and to their teachers
who must provide the understanding and the knowledge.

Contents

Preface

This syllabus has been written primarily for kindergarten and first-grade teachers to use with their classes. Others will also find it useful, particularly teachers of the mentally retarded and speech clinicians who work with groups. Since the development and stabilization of normal patterns of oral communication is a cherished goal in our society, we begin to focus our attention early on how our children talk. Though only 10 to 20 percent of the kindergarten and first-grade children will have speech sound errors, all of them need opportunities to modify their oral communication.

These speech improvement materials were planned to enable children who use them to learn to listen to others as well as to themselves, to make judgments about their own speech and that of others, and to utilize normal speech patterns when they talk. The lessons are organized around the speech sounds that are most likely to be defective, and the activities have been selected to achieve specific goals in relation to these sounds. The creative teacher will be able to supplement these ideas and will incorporate them in most of the other curricular offerings.

Since many of the people who will use this syllabus will have had a limited background in speech development, detailed instructions for using this syllabus have been provided. In addition, both a brief account of how children learn to talk, and how the teacher can best utilize speech correction facilities have been included.

The materials for the original syllabus were prepared in 1959 as a part of Research Project 620 (8255) which was supported by the Cooperative Research Branch of the U.S. Office of Education. The present revision incorporates many of the ideas from the first one and supplementary suggestions provided by the teachers who have used copies of the syllabus.

This text might never have materialized without the encouragement and able assistance of many people. Two graduate students in speech pathology, Mrs. Lauren Wilson and Mrs. Theo Penny, should receive special mention. They worked with the author in developing trial lessons as a part of their master's theses, and also conducted a program with kindergarten classes. Dr. John A. Dewar, currently a member of the staff of the Department of Education at Northern Illinois University, checked the vocabulary and language structure of the original syllabus.

The administrators of two public school systems, Wichita and Lawrence,

Kansas, provided the opportunity to try out this approach to speech learning. Dr. Alvin E. Morris, Associate Superintendent in charge of elementary education in the Wichita Public Schools, and Dr. Eldon Breazier, the Curriculum Director of the Lawrence Public Schools at that time, arranged for the author to utilize their respective school systems for the initial project. Through the efforts of Dr. Robert Ohlsen, Director of Special Education in the Wichita Public Schools, and Mr. William McClelland, Director of Speech and Hearing Services in the Lawrence Public Schools, teachers were encouraged to volunteer for the project.

Eight first-grade and ten kindergarten teachers were selected from more than 100 volunteers to carry out the program for one year. All of them received a limited amount of in-service training during that year, and the author visited their classrooms while they were conducting the speech improvement program. They were an enthusiastic group with a primary concern for the speech development of the children in their classes. Though some of them had misgivings about this approach at the beginning, by the end of the school year most of them were convinced by both the accelerated learning of their classes and their own involvement in the program that speech improvement work is an important phase of the language arts curricula. Most of these teachers have continued to use the syllabus with their new classes each year.

The speech clinicians in the two communities cooperated with this program in many ways. First of all they too were enthusiastic. They added to their caseloads children whom the author recommended and did not schedule those for whom we requested a delay. Miss Betty Berry, presently the Director of the Speech and Hearing Programs in the Kansas State Department of Public Instruction, volunteered to help with the testing of the children for the three-year period. Without her assistance the task of evaluating the hundreds of children would have been endless.

The children who were a part of the study represented all levels of socio-economic status and were a cross-section of children enrolled in public schools in a large city system and a university town. They maintained their interest in speech improvement throughout the year, and most of them demonstrated their newly acquired speech skills for the three years we followed them in the testing program.

Many faculty members at the University of Kansas discussed this approach to speech learning with the author. Dr. Robert Ridgway, Associate Dean of the School of Education in charge of Elementary Education, and Dr. Richard Schiefelbusch, Director of the Bureau of Child Research, were particularly helpful.

Special appreciation should be expressed to Mrs. Eleanor Schlissel, our Clinic secretary, who not only typed the manuscript for this text, but prepared the mimeographed copies of the original syllabus, that were requested by over 1000 teachers and clinicians.

MARGARET C. BYRNE

THE CHILD SPEAKS

Introduction

SPEECH AND LANGUAGE DEVELOPMENT

During the first weeks of school the teacher will be learning about the children in her room through observation of their behavior and through listening to them as they talk with her and with one another. Through classroom activities and parent conferences she will be ascertaining which children are the most self-sufficient, which ones seem immature, and which ones exhibit special problems. She will note the cultural background of her group and attempt to determine the types of experiences which constitute most of the out-of-school time of the children.

One of the keys to understanding children will be the manner in which they communicate. The majority in the kindergarten and first-grade age group, except perhaps for the culturally deprived, will be communicating in language patterns that are similar to those of the adult in syntax, though not in size of vocabulary. They will be using most of the sounds of our language accurately. Gestures and movement will accompany their words. Much of the content of their speech will be egocentric.

Since speech is learned by the child in a defined environment, it will reflect all of the influences and experiences he has had in the home, his peer relationships, his own perceptions of himself, and his attitudes. What he has been able to learn will be dependent upon what physical and intellectual attributes he has, and his psychological readiness.

Because the child must use the sounds of our language correctly if his expressed ideas are to be understood, the teacher is concerned about the normal acquisition of phonemes and why some children do not have intelligible speech when they enter school. During the early months of a child's life he uses all speech sounds in his vocalizations. As he listens to and is stimulated by those in his environment, he tries to imitate what he hears. One child in his initial attempts may approximate the normal speech he has heard. As he grows older, those first approximations may change to inaccuracies, or they may stabilize as correct phonemes. Another child may imitate accurately in his early efforts and continue to use those phonemes correctly. Thus even if the child's model has had normal articulatory patterns, the child may or may not develop accuracy in articulation.

Some of the most common error patterns are readily identifiable to the teacher who has trained herself to listen. Typical consonantal substitution errors include the following: *w* for *r* and *l*, as in *red* and *lamp*; voiceless *th* for *s*, as in *sun*; voiced *th* for *z*, as in *zebra*; *f* for the voiceless *th*, as in *thumb; d* for the voiced *th* and *g,* as in *this* and *get; b* for *v,* as in *valentine; s* or *ch* for *sh,* as in *shoe;* and *t* for *k* as in *candy.* In addition the child may produce a sound correctly, but use it in inappropriate places. For instance he may say *fis* for *fish* and yet not use the *s* when he says *soup.* When the sound substitution pattern is a consistent one, the listener tends to fill in the correct sound, and then the child's speech appears to be more intelligible.

When the child is learning the sounds in words, he tends to more frequently use the phonemes correctly if they occur at the beginning of words. The sounds in the final position may be stabilized more slowly. This may be part of the reason why those children who have primarily an omission pattern will omit the consonants at the end of words.

Although we do not know what specific forces have operated to retard the speech learning of a child, we recognize that the inaccurate patterns can be a deterrent in the development of his ego and therefore in his school work. As a result we should encourage the child to modify his speech. The learning experiences of a speech improvement program provide one means of bringing about the many necessary changes.

Since the classroom teacher is not the "expert" in speech pathology, she should not hesitate to ask for assistance from those whose primary task is speech rehabilitation. Her role, however, is a vital one in directing the speech learning of children, and she can utilize her classroom as an ideal setting in which children imitate her good speech patterns, modify their own, and develop more adequate oral communication skills.

Clinical Speech Resources

The speech clinician is an important resource person for the classroom teacher. He fulfills many functions, depending upon his interests and the scope of his program. He may be the consultant for the speech improvement program, and carry out both the in-service training of the teachers and the speech testing of the children. If he is responsible for the speech improvement program, he will work closely with the classroom teacher.

Even if the speech clinician is not supervising speech improvement work, he will be able to assist the teacher in many ways. The teacher should talk with him about the children whose speech patterns in her judgment are too deviate for her to modify. She may recommend that the speech clinician schedule these children for a complete speech and language evaluation; and if they are included in the speech therapy program, she will want to know how to work with them in her improvement program. If she feels that the speech problem of a child is complicated by variables such as hearing loss, emotional problems, retardation, and other factors, she should arrange for additional conferences with the speech clinician concerning the child and her perceptions of him.

If the teacher is working in a school setting where no speech clinicians are on the staff, she may have to investigate possible referral sources for some of her children. The State Department of Public Instruction, through its Division of Special Education, usually will have lists of public school and private speech clinics, and may also have the names of qualified speech clinicians in private practice. Many universities will have speech and hearing clinics to which children can be referred for evaluation and therapy. The Executive Secretary of the American Speech and Hearing Association (1001 Connecticut Avenue, N.W., Washington, D.C.) has lists of members in each state who hold clinical certification.

DIRECTIONS FOR USING THE SYLLABUS

TIME

The syllabus has been organized so that a minimum of one week is devoted to each unit. The units on *s* and the voiceless *th* cover eight and ten days respectively. There is no need to follow the order of sound presentation, if the teacher has reasons for changing it. However, it seemed appropriate from the point of view of the Christmas holiday activities and materials that would hold prime interest for the children, to have the review of the first four sounds come just prior to the Christmas vacation. Work on the *v* sound has been scheduled for the Valentine Day period, because of the special appeal of valentines to young children.

Since both teacher and children need time to become acquainted, many of the teachers who have used this syllabus start the program about November 1. By then the teacher knows which children need the most help in speech, and in general what problems she must work on. She could then complete the lessons about the middle of April and review the sounds that were most difficult for her group during the last six weeks of the term.

The daily lessons have been planned for 15 to 30 minutes. Teachers who have used the material found that for both kindergarten and first grade, the attention of the children was held for the most part for 20 to 30 minutes. If the teacher wishes to expand these materials and/or to add others that fit in with the goal of the lesson, she should feel free to do so. The related activities can be scheduled as frequently as the teacher is able to work them into the program. Some of the kindergarten teachers utilized the ideas in the syllabus as a core curriculum. Note that the material in bold-face indicates instructions for the teacher only.

OVER–ALL PROGRAMMING

In order for the teacher to present the lessons as effectively as possible, it is suggested that she be very familiar with the materials. She will want to preview the filmstrip and records so that she knows how to present them to her group. The pictures will have to be selected and the objects must be readily available.

Throughout the program, she should stress the sound which is being presented, to overemphasize it in the initial presentation, in the story materials, and the section on discrimination. She should always refer to the sound, not to the *letter* of the alphabet. For instance it's the *k* sound not the *kay* sound. This approach will make it easier for children later when they learn in reading that the *k* sound has several spellings.

Because the child's failure to develop normal speech patterns may be due to many causes, there may be some children in the group who make little progress. The teacher should do the best she can with these children, remembering that she is not expected to be an experienced speech clinician. She may want to talk with the speech clinician about such children. Within the limits of this material and her own training, she will help those children to use the group experiences to their best advantage. She is encouraged to single out children for sections of the program, but to do so in moderation. None of us want a child to feel defeated because he can't seem to do what his teacher expects of him.

It is suggested that the class develop a scrap book, with the children bringing in pictures which they have found with the sound that is being stressed. The assignment to find pictures should be introduced after the children have identified the sound and listened for it.

INTRODUCTION OF THE PROGRAM

In order to encourage the children to remember the purpose of these activities, a few items have been suggested for use each day. The teacher begins each lesson with Mr. Frog and the Listening Ears. Mr. Frog introduces each new sound, and the Listening Ears help the children to learn about the sounds. Children can take turns in distributing the imaginary ears, and also in bringing out the frog and returning him to his place. The Sound Box can be especially useful in those sessions where objects and pictures are used. Since new materials will be utilized each day the reappearance of these familiar objects will add continuity to the program, and will help the children to tie the program into a meaningful part of the year's activities. (At least, the teachers who have used the syllabus found these daily reminders very useful.)

Unit 1—Sounds Around Us

The first unit emphasizes the development of good listening habits. The children should be encouraged to listen for gross environmental noises and to discriminate among the more discrete sounds of people's voices and pitch patterns. Although the teacher may spend only a week or two on these activities, all of the succeeding lessons stress the skill of listening and its role in enabling children to make finer and finer discriminations among the sounds used in talking.

Also, during this unit the teacher identifies the parts of the body which are used in talking—the lips, jaw, tongue, teeth, and roof of the mouth, particularly. It is hoped that this information will be used cautiously throughout the program; children need not be so conscious of tongue placement, for instance, that they forget to listen, look, and feel.

Units 2, 3, 4, 5, 7, 8, 9, 10, 12, 13, 14, 15, 17, 18—Special Sounds

Activities of these units are built around specific sounds. Each unit has the general goal of helping the children to identify one sound, to listen, to discriminate between it and other sounds, and to produce it correctly in controlled situations. In addition activities have been recommended which should encourage the children to engage in successful speaking experiences. The materials can be presented in a sequence such as the following daily schedule. For some sounds, however, the teacher may want to spend more time on some subgoals. Sufficient ideas have been presented so that she can concentrate longer on those aspects of learning the sound that seem to be most pertinent for her class.

First Day: Identification of the Sound. After the children have put on their imaginary Listening Ears Mr. Frog introduces the new sound through the association of the sound with an animal, an object, or a popular figure. For instance the *p* sound is associated with the pig, which may now be taken from the Sound Box. Then the children are asked to think of various categories of names which have the *p* sound in them. At this stage the children should be thinking about the words in which *they* use the sound. This type of silent internalization of the way that words sound requires the use of judgment on their part to accept some words and reject others. Also, in this lesson the children should, wherever possible, have a visual picture of how they make the sound, and how the teacher and the child's peers make it. No lengthy discussion is needed. The very simple directions, plus the use of the mirror, will enable them to see the position of the speech helpers as they produce the sound alone, and in combination with other sounds. Each child should receive kinaesthetic sensation of how it feels as he makes the sounds of our language. For example he can *feel* the tongue as it rests momentarily on the back portion of the roof of the mouth as he says a *k* sound.

After identification of the sound for the children in as many ways as possible, they are asked to remember what they have learned until the next day when another skill will be added.

Second Day: Listening for the Sound. Mr. Frog again helps to distribute the Listening Ears. He is interested in knowing whether the children remember what sound they are stressing, who makes the sound, and whether he can hear them make it in unison, in small groups, and in some cases individually.

Then the teacher asks the children to listen carefully to the story she will tell them. In some instances she'll be using a book, and will want the children to tell her the names of specific pictures before she starts her story. Also, in many of the stories the children use the sound in isolation at stated places as a response. While she tells the story, the teacher is to emphasize the key words (those which contain the sound being stressed and carry the main thread of the story.)

After the story has been told or read, discussion of it may center around the experiences the children have had which relate to the story; they may be asked questions about the story, which they are encouraged to answer in complete sentences; or they may recreate portions of the tale. Whatever the activity may be, the teacher should keep in mind that the goal here is not only general listening and remembering of the story, but also the special words in this story having the sound on which the children are working. Lots of other words of course won't have the special sound. The children should not be so carried away by the story and its activities that they forget its importance as a tool in developing discrete listening habits.

Third Day: Discriminating Between the New Sound and Other Sounds. After the Listening Ears are on and Mr. Frog has been taken from the Sound Box, Mr. Frog helps again to remind the class that his companion for the day, whether it's Mr. Pig, or the Grey Goose, has some new activities to introduce. The children again identify the key object and make "his" sound.

At this point the teacher is ready to ask the children to make judgments about whether names of pictures do or do not contain the special sound. This type of activity requires that children recognize the sound auditorily, although they may not produce it correctly. This session primarily utilizes pictures of objects. Some pictures have the special sound in their names, but others do not. The children are asked to place the picture in front of the key object if it has the special sound; and to give it to Mr. Frog if it doesn't. For instance in Unit 2 a picture of the pencil would be given to Mr. Pig, but the one of a ball would go to Mr. Frog. As the year's program progresses, and the children learn to carry out this activity successfully, the teacher may want to ask about the names of pictures that have the sounds covered in earlier sessions.

Because this process of learning to discriminate is difficult for some children, additional motivation may be introduced by assigning leaders for each week, who can then select the children to whom the pictures are to be given. Or the procedures for naming the pictures can be varied from one sound to another. One teacher had the children place the pictures without the special sound on a train that was on an imaginary siding, because those pictures would have to wait until a later day for their trip.

After the pictures have been classified as those with, and those without, the sound, the teacher may want to place several of them on a flannel board or holder, and ask specific children to name a picture and tell whether it has the special sound. She may want to repeat the names of some of the children, for further learning in discrimination.

This session ends with the reassurance that new activities will be introduced at the next session.

Fourth Day: Producing the Correct Sound.   After Mr. Frog, the Listening Ears, and the identifying article for the week's sound have been set out, the children may be asked to describe what activity had been carried out the previous day. They may also be asked individually or as a class to produce the sound in isolation.

The purpose of this day's activities is the utilization of the correct production of the special sound in controlled situations. Many different types of activities are suggested for this day's program. Sometimes a rhyme is used or the children may play grocery store or some other game in which they use carrier phrases. For example when the sound *p* is being stressed in Unit 2, Lesson IV, children use the phrase, "I'll put _____ on our boat," in one of the activities. The first part of the sentence, "I'll put," would be considered the carrier phrase.

When a child is unable to correctly produce the sound for that unit, after he has identified it, listened for it, and discriminated between it and other sounds, the teacher should observe what he says in place of the correct sound and what he does with the articulators. For instance as he says the word, *shoe,* does he say *sue* or *thu?* Does he spread his lips, instead of rounding them for the *sh;* or does he protrude his tongue and therefore substitute a *th?* The teacher should overemphasize the correct production for the child, asking him to imitate her as she says it in isolation, and then asking him to try to put the correct sound in the word, like this—*sh—oe,* then *shoe.* She should place the emphasis on the positive approach; and wherever possible, let the experience be a successful one. Even partial success is better than complete failure. Try this procedure once or twice and then drop it for a time. Or it might be possible to have the entire class, or one child carry out the procedure correctly, as another ear-training device.

Fifth Day: Carry-over of Correct Production in Sharing Time. The teacher, using the key objects such as Mr. Frog, as motivational devices, structures sharing time so that the children will employ the suggested carrier phrase or phrases as they describe what they have brought to school. If time permits, she may select a few of the articles brought by the children for additional class practice in the correct production of the special sound. If children are not encouraged to bring toys for sharing time, it will be necessary to plan to use the carrier phrases in whatever programs provide speaking activities for the children. If the teacher spends some time each day in *sharing,* rather than on any preselected day, she should arrange for each child to use a carrier phrase that seems pertinent for the child and will provide practice for the specific sound.

Units 6, 11, 16, 19—Review Sessions

During these weeks review sessions will be held. Since the learning of speech sounds is to be cumulative, the review should be given during specific periods. During the final week all of the sounds covered in the program will be reviewed.

The program for these weeks will be slightly different from the initial presentation of the sounds. The basic goals of identification, discrimination, and correct production of the sounds however will be stressed again. Many of the materials from the preceding weeks, such as Mr. Frog and Listening Ears, will be utilized.

On the *first* day of the review week the four sounds will be associated with the identifying items. The children should be encouraged to use visual, auditory, and kinaesthetic cues to identify each sound. Production of the sound in isolation will be a part of the activities.

The *second* day's activities will stress discrimination. During the weeks when voiced and voiceless pairs are reviewed, such as *s* and *z*, the differences between the two sounds will be brought out. Also, words will be introduced which contain two of the four sounds in the review unit. The teacher will overemphasize the sounds during this period, also.

On the *third* day the program will combine the discrimination and production. It is suggested at this point that the teacher should not overemphasize the sound patterns.

Both the *fourth* and *fifth* days will stress correct production of the four sounds in words and carrier phrases. Sharing time will provide opportunities for the children to practice the sounds and to stabilize normal production in conversation.

Incorporation of the Sound in Other Classroom Activities

At the end of the lessons on each sound some suggestions are given for helping the children to be aware of the speech program in many of the activities in which they engage. The following ideas can be applied to each sound. Some classes may try to draw or color the identifying items. The best ones, or all of them, could be posted around the room, or on the bulletin boards in the hall. Some classes may be able to show their materials in the school's display cabinets. Many physical education activities can be adapted, so that the class can imitate the walk of the animals, or play games which stress the special sound. In music the children learn to identify high and low notes and different musical instruments—a skill which requires one kind of discrimination. Teachers can select stories for reading that have many key words with the sound being learned. There will be countless ways to modify the curriculum, so that it is intertwined with each day's speech program.

No attempt has been made to give specific ways that the first-grade teacher can incorporate the visual learning of the letters of the alphabet with the auditory presentation. Since reading is developed in many ways by different teachers, it seemed best to encourage each to work out her own related activities. She might, for instance, want to point out to the children that the name of the child in the reader begins with the sound they have called the Teakettle sound, or the Jack-in-the-Box sound. During word building activities she might wish to utilize the vocabulary of the speech improvement program.

Materials to Be Used with the Syllabus

The appendixes have been set up to provide information about the materials to be used with the various units. Appendix A provides the suggestions for each unit, the approximate cost of the items, and sources from which each can be obtained. If the teacher prefers to cut out her own pictures, she will not need the Bryngelson-Glasby cards. However, the prepared cards save valuable time. In each unit where pictures are used, the numbers after the words refer to the Bryngelson-Glasby cards. Some of the pictures that are suggested are not available in the set, however, and the teacher will either have to draw them or find them in magazines.

Appendixes B and C provide additional references. Appendix B lists stories having many key words for the sound of the week, which the teacher might read to her class. The list is by no means an exhaustive one, but can be used with discretion by the teacher. Appropriate storybooks and a comment about music books will be found in Appendix C.

Since many of the pictures are used in several different units, their names are alphabetized together with their appropriate units, in Appendix D. If the teacher wishes, she may want to set up her own filing system for these pictures, so that she will be able to pull the necessary ones quickly.

General Outline of the Goals and Activities for Each Sound

   I. Introducing the sound:
      A. Association of the sound with the name of an animal and/or a familiar object.
      B. Words in which we find it.
         1. Identification of children whose names begin with the sound.
         2. Objects or animals that make the sound.
         3. Colors or numbers with the sound.
  II. Listening for the sound:
      A. A story which stresses vocabulary that requires the sound.
      B. Opportunities for the children to produce the sound in isolation.
      C. Questions based on the story or other activities that stress answers which utilize the sound.
 III. Discriminating between the new sound and other sounds:
      A. Picture materials or games which require children to determine whether or not the sound is present in specific words.
 IV. Producing the correct sound in words:
      A. Action games.
      B. Stories.
      C. Activities.
  V. Sharing time—carry-over of correct sound production during show and tell:
      A. Utilization by the children of a key phrase which includes the sound being stressed.

Incorporation of the sound in other classroom activities:
1. In art work.
2. In physical education.
3. In numbers.
4. In reading and reading readiness.
5. In story telling.

ORDER OF PRESENTATION OF MATERIALS

Unit	Central Theme	Identifying Object
1	Sounds around us	
2	*p* sound	Mr. Pig
3	*k* sound	Captain Kangaroo
4	*s* sound	Tommy Teakettle
5	*z* sound	Buzzing Bee
6	Review of *p, k, s, z*	
7	*g* sound	Grey Goose
8	*sh* sound	Seashell
9	*l* sound	Telephone
10	*f* sound	Funny Face Clown
11	Review of *g, sh, l, f*	
12	*v* sound	Valentine
13	*ch* sound	Choo Choo the Train
14	*j* sound	Jack-in-the-Box
15	*r* sound	Red Rooster
16	Review of *v, ch, l, r*	
17	Voiced *th* sound	Airplane
18	Unvoiced *th* sound	Thumperina
19	Review of entire program	

UNIT 1

Sounds Around Us

LESSON I *INTRODUCTION*

(Note: Bold-face material indicates instructions for the teacher only.)

[MATERIALS]   Mr. Frog, Listening Ears, bell, whistle, baby rattle, a piece of paper, and any other noisemakers that children might know.

Wherever we are, there are sounds. Some of them are so loud that we can't ignore them, like the banging of the drum. What are some others? (**Boys and girls on the playground, fire engines, screeching of brakes.**) Then there are the quiet sounds for which we must listen intently—like whispering voices, and a bird singing. What quiet sounds can you think of?

Each day we are going to listen for sounds, learn as much as we can about them, and use them. Things make sounds—and so do people. We're going to have several helpers—Mr. Frog (**pull him out of the Sound Box**), our Listening Ears (**put one set on, and tell the class they'll have "pretend" Listening Ears**), and of course, all of you.

Let's see how well you use your Listening Ears. I'm going to make some sounds, and you tell me what they are. Close your eyes—**shake baby rattle, etc. (After each one have the children as a group tell you what they heard. Follow the same procedure as you tear paper, clap hands, snap fingers.)**

Most of the sounds you listened for today were made by things. Tomorrow we'll be listening to many additional kinds of sounds. Now let's tell Mr. Frog "goodbye," and put our Listening Ears in the Sound Box.

LESSON II *ADDITIONAL SOUNDS AROUND US*

[MATERIALS]   Records, such as *Muffin in the City, Muffin in the Country*, and *Let's Listen.*

It's time for us to open our Sound Box. Who can guess what's inside? A dog, a cow? No, Mr. Frog. What else is in the bag? Our Listening Ears. Who wants to help me give them all to you? What else do you think might be in the Sound Box? It's round and it must be played on a record player. Certainly, it's a record, but a very special record. As I play it for you, you'll have to listen in order to tell who or what made the sounds. Today we'll take turns in answering. I'll play a part of the record, then someone will tell me what made the sound. Listen for animal sounds and then for others.

Now let's listen to the sounds we hear around us. Who can tell us what is making the sounds outside? (**These sounds will depend upon the location of the school—cars, train whistles, adult voices, screeching of brakes, rain, occasionally a child's voice, various birds. Determine how many are outside the room, then any that are in the room—like a dripping faucet, a clock, shuffling of feet, tapping of fingers on a desk, leafing through a book, and moving of chairs.**)

Our Listening Ears help us to hear more sounds around us. Tomorrow we'll try to listen for other sources of sounds. **Note: This lesson can extend over two or three days, depending upon the records available and the children's interests.**

LESSON III *OUR VOICES*

Mr. Frog wants to distribute the Listening Ears to you today. He can't make any sounds for which you can listen, but he wants all of you to listen as *you* make sounds. First, let's divide the class in half. (**Have them count one—two. Then all the one's will line up on one side and the two's on the other side of the teacher after directions are given.**) We'll name those children with the number one our puppies, and the number two's will be the pussy cats. I'm going to ask the puppies to close their eyes in a minute. While they have their eyes closed, I'll tap on the shoulder of one of the pussy cats and that person will say, "Hello, how are you." Then the puppies who know who has spoken will tell us. We'll try three different pussy cats; then, three puppies while the pussy cats close their eyes. All set? Pussies line up on the left, the puppies on my right. Puppies, close your eyes. (**Select children whose voices are different—some children with quiet voices, others with loud voices. This activity can be repeated several times if the attention of the children is good. Other phrases like, What's my name? Today is Wednesday, or I'm a puppy, what are you? can also be used.**)

Now let's all sit down, and we'll try something else with our voices. We all sing up the scale like this—do, re, mi, fa, so, la, ti, do. Let's put words to this melody, and see if we can sing in tune. (**Start off with a comfortable pitch, and have the children sing one line on each of the pitches. Any verses can be used. Some teachers prefer to have the children count one to eight instead of using the scale symbols.**)

LESSON IV *SPEECH HELPERS*

[MATERIALS]   **Mirrors.**

REVIEW

Yesterday we learned that we could identify one another's voices, and that we could make our voices go up and down on key. Today we'll learn about the parts of our body that help us to talk.

ACTIVITIES

1. First we'll put on our Listening Ears. Then we'll ask Mr. Frog to help us find our speech helpers. (**On the frog, identify the lips, jaw, tongue, nose, roof of the mouth, voice box, and breathing machine. Put his lips together as you say *m;* raise the tip of his tongue to the roof of his mouth as you say *l.*)**

2. Now we're going to look at our own talking helpers. (**Distribute the mirrors, so that each child can observe his lips, jaw, tongue, and teeth.**) While each of you looks in the mirror, observe what you do with your lips when you make the following sounds: *m, ee, oo-ee, oo-ee-oo-ee.* Now watch your jaws as you say *ee, a* (**father**). What do you do with your teeth when you say *s-s-s-, th, ee, I, hello?* (**Ask the children to describe the position of the teeth, tongue, and jaw after they have said each sound and word.**)

3. Our tongue helps us in making the sounds we use in talking. Watch it as you say *la, la, la; ta, ta, ta.* What happens to it? Try *ka, ka, ka; ga, ga, ga.* What part of the tongue do we use? The back of the tongue moves up to meet the roof of the mouth, doesn't it?

4. We'll put our mirrors away, and stand up. Take in a deep breath, hold it a minute, and let it go. (**Do this activity several times, until the children get the idea that they can take in a little or a great deal of air.**) We don't need a great deal of air for talking, but we must have some. When we run, we get out of breath, and then we can't talk for a few seconds. When we want to talk very loudly, we need more air. When you shout on the playground, you use more air. In what other activities do you use more air?

5. Some of our speech sounds need a voice box and others don't. We can feel on our throats when we have the motor turned on. Let's try saying *a* (**father**) and put your three fingers on your throat, just as I'm doing. (**Place them at the level of the Adam's apple on the man's throat, which is the level of the thyroid cartilage in women.**) Now try *p, p, p, p, p.* There's no voice. What about *tt, oo, ee, d, s?* Do you use your voices for all of these? (**For all but the *s.*)**

SUMMARY

Today, we looked at our speech helpers, and we watched how they work in making sounds. Tomorrow, we shall identify them in other ways.

LESSON V   *MORE ABOUT OUR SPEECH HELPERS*

[MATERIALS]   **Filmstrip, *Our Talking Helpers.***

REVIEW

Mr. Frog wants to know how well you remember his speech helpers. Even though he doesn't talk, he has many of the same ones we do. Who wants to tell us about Mr. Frog's speech helpers? (**Encourage a couple of children to take the frog and point out his tongue, lips, jaw, breathing machine, and roof of the mouth.**)

ACTIVITIES

Our filmstrip is next. We'll watch and then we'll follow some directions that I'll give you. (**Use as many frames of the filmstrip as your children will permit. Read the material to them as you show the frames; or just tell them what is occurring. In those sections where you can ask the children to carry out an activity with you, do so. You may wish to show portions of the filmstrip on successive days.**)

SUMMARY

We've been learning about the parts of our bodies that help us to talk, and about how important our ears are. Mr. Frog and our Listening Ears will stay in our Sound Box until tomorrow, when they'll return to tell us about the sounds we use in talking. Let's say goodbye to Mr. Frog.

[ADDITIONAL ACTIVITIES FOR THIS UNIT]
1. Have children make sets of Listening Ears to wear.
2. Check Appendixes B and C for other stories and songs for listening.

UNIT 2

p Sound—Mr. Pig

LESSON I *INTRODUCTION*

The p sound is presented first because it is easy for the children to visualize and is used correctly by most of them.

[MATERIALS]   **Mr. Frog, Listening Ears, and Mr. Pig.**

REVIEW

Mr. Frog is back with us again today. Who can tell me what speech helpers we use in talking? Who wants to show us these speech helpers on Mr. Frog? Does he have a voice box? Yes, but he doesn't talk with words as we do. Where are our speech helpers? (**Have the children point to their jaws, teeth, lips, tongue, roof of the mouth, voice box, and breathing machine.**) Why did Mr. Frog give us Listening Ears? Shall we put them on now?

ACTIVITIES

Our Sound Box has a surprise for us. It's something that lives on a farm; it has a big nose; it's not a cow; it says "oink, oink" when it's hungry or happy. What is it? Yes, it's a pig. Mr. Pig's name begins with a p. Mr. Frog says p by putting his lips together. Let's hear all of you say p. Now let's have the girls do it, now the boys.

Some of you may have names that begin with p. Let's see. Who thinks his name begins with a p? (**Have the children indicate whose names begin with p. If they can't get started, suggest some, like Patty, Paul, Perry, Peter, Priscilla, Pamela, Patricia, Peggy, Pearl, Polly.**) Can any of you hear the p sound in your last names?

Some of you know colors that have the p sound in them. What are they? (**Purple, pink**)

We have many things in this room with the p sound—things we see and use every day. Who knows some of them? (**Paper, pictures, pencil, paint, pan, paste**)

Who can guess what I'm thinking of that has a p in it?

Something we eat for dessert (**Pie**)
Something we made for Halloween (**Pumpkin**)

The name of the meal we eat when we go home from school (**Supper**)
A coin (**Penny**)
The animal who came to visit us today (**Pig**)

Tomorrow we're going to have a story about Mr. Pig. We'll put Mr. Frog, Mr. Pig, and our Listening Ears in the Sound Box until tomorrow.

LESSON II *LISTENING*

[MATERIALS]   **Mr. Frog, Mr. Pig, and Listening Ears.**

REVIEW

Yesterday Mr. Frog introduced us to Mr. Pig. Today they are both ready to pass out the Listening Ears, so that we can have our story. You all know the story of *The Three Pigs*. We're going to act out the story today.

ACTIVITY

Our story needs some volunteers. We must have Mr. Wolf, Peter Pig, Pat Pig, and Paul Pig. Who wants to be Mr. Wolf? Peter Pig, Pat Pig, and Paul Pig? The rest of you are going to be the three houses that the three pigs built. Let's have the rest of you count one, two, three. Now all the one's will be with Paul and his straw house; the two's will be with Pat and her wooden house; and the three's will be with Peter and his stone house.

Before we start the story, we'd better practice what each one says:

> Mr. Wolf goes: *puff, puff, puff*
> Straw and wood houses: *p, p, p*
> Stone house: *pu, pu, pu*

Are we all ready? Those who are the straw house form a circle; wooden house, another; and the stone house a third circle. We'll stand up until Mr. Wolf blows down the houses. I'll help you to remember when you are to join in the story.

THE THREE PIGS[1]

Once upon a time there were three little pigs. Their names were Paul and Peter and Pat. They lived with Mama Pig and Papa Pig in Sleepy Valley.

One day Mama Pig called to Paul and Peter and Pat, and this is what she said: "Papa Pig and I are getting old. We can't work hard enough now to feed you and buy your clothes."

So Paul and Peter and Pat Pig said good-by to Mama and Papa Pig and started down the path in front of their house. Soon they saw some straw in

---

[1] Theo M. Penny, The Development and Evaluation of a Speech Improvement Program for Kindergarten Children. Unpublished Master's thesis, University of Kansas, 1960, Appendix B.

a field. Paul said: "Peter and Pat, I am going to stop here and build my house of straw." So Peter and Pat left him to build his house and they travelled on down the path.

Soon Peter and Pat saw some sticks beneath a tree. Pat said: "Peter, I am going to stop here and build my house of wood." So Peter left Pat to build her house. He travelled on down the path.

Finally Peter saw an old stone fence which was beginning to fall down. He stopped and thought to himself (for there wasn't anyone for him to talk to): "I'm going to stop here and build my house of stone." And he set to work.

Peter and Pat and Paul had their houses all built. Now there is someone else in this story. There is the Big Bad Wolf. The Big Bad Wolf just loved to eat little pigs for dinner—or supper—or even breakfast.

One day the Big Bad Wolf walked by Mama and Papa Pig's house. He didn't see Paul or Pat or Peter and he wondered where they were. So he walked on down the path. Soon he came to a field; all the straw was gone. Right in the middle of the field stood a house made of straw, a pig's house!

The Big Bad Wolf went up to the door of Paul Pig's house and knocked. He said. "Little Pig, Little Pig, let me in." But Paul Pig would not open the door. He just answered: "Not by the hair of your chinny-chin-chin, I'll not let you in." So the Big Bad Wolf said: "I'll puff and I'll puff till I blow your house in." And he went: "Puff, puff, puff, puff." And as he blew, the straw house went "P, p, p, p," getting weaker and weaker all the time. Paul Pig ran out the back door. The Wolf went, "Puff, puff, puff, puff," again, and he blew the house in. Paul Pig ran to the house of his sister Pat Pig.

The Big Bad Wolf was very angry. He went tramping down the path. Soon he saw another Pig's house. He hurried up to the house and knocked. He said: "Little Pig, Little Pig, let me in." And Pat and Paul answered: "Not by the hair of your chinny-chin-chin, we'll not let you in." So the Big Bad Wolf said: "I'll puff, and I'll puff till I blow your house in." And he went "Puff, puff, puff, puff." And as he blew, the wood house went "P, p, p, p," getting weaker and weaker all the time. Paul and Pat ran out the back door. The Wolf went: "Puff, puff, puff, puff," again, and he blew the house in. Paul and Pat ran to the house of their brother Peter Pig.

Now the Big Bad Wolf was very, very angry because he had puffed and puffed and blown down two houses and he still didn't have any little pigs for supper. He went tramp-tramping down the path. Soon he saw another pig's house. He hurried up to the house and knocked. He said: "Little Pig, Little Pig, let me in." And Peter and Pat and Paul answered: "Not by the hair of your chinny-chin-chin, we'll not let you in." So the Big Bad Wolf said: "I'll puff, and I'll puff till I blow your house in." And he went "Puff, puff, puff, puff." And as he blew, the strong stone house went "Pu, pu, pu, pu." And the Wolf blew again, "Puff, puff, puff, puff." He puffed so hard that he fell down the steps and broke two legs and his nose and ended up in the hospital. The Big Bad Wolf finally got out of the hospital, but he still has to walk on crutches, and now he goes "Puff, puff, puff, puff," all the time instead of just when he is trying to blow down houses. And Peter, Paul, and Pat Pig aren't afraid of him anymore because now they can run faster than he can. And besides, they live together in the strong stone house that goes "Pu, pu, pu, pu."

Let's see if Mr. Frog can say *p, p, p,* before we put him away. Mr. Wolf, would you gather up the Listening Ears and put them in the Sound Box for me? Tomorrow we'll have another surprise.

LESSON III *DISCRIMINATION*

[MATERIALS]   Mr. Frog, Mr. Pig, Listening Ears, and pictures whose names will be used in the lesson.

REVIEW

Who remembers the names of the three pigs in our story yesterday? What did the wolf say as he blew down the two houses? What did the houses say? What was different about Peter's house? As it stood up under Mr. Wolf's puffing, what did it say?

ACTIVITIES

We know that everything doesn't have the *p* sound in its name. Mr. Frog has brought along some pictures for us, and he wants us to tell him if these things have names with the *p* sound. Let's put our Listening Ears on, and as I show the pictures to you, you tell its name. If you think it has the *p* sound, then you tell me to put the picture in front of Mr. Pig. If it doesn't, you tell me to put the picture in front of Mr. Frog. We'll take turns. (**If you prefer, a child can distribute the pictures or each one can come up and draw one from the Sound Box. The numeral after the name of the picture indicates the number of the Bryngelson-Glasby card.**)

PICTURES WITH *p*		PICTURES WITHOUT *p*	
pencil-2	paint	girls-16	baby
spoon-4	pan	boy-27	bed
policeman-8	paper	boat-36	bird
plane-37	pear	fire-79	butter
cup-55	penny	bear-92	hammer
cap-58	potatoes	brush-102	meat
pumpkin-145	top	bunny rabbit-118	milk
lips		balls-151	

Let's count the pictures we gave to Mr. Pig and the ones we gave to Mr. Frog.

I know a rhyme that I think you will like. It goes like this:

Hippety hop, hippety hop
Skip, skip, flip, flop
Hippety hop, hippety hop
Skip, skip, now stop.

We'll say it together. We'll form a circle, and we'll use actions with the poem. We'll hop as we do the first line; then we'll skip and move our bodies from side to side; then we'll hop, and skip, then stop. All set?

Back to our seats! Leave your Listening Ears in the Sound Box as you go. We'll need them tomorrow when Mr. Pig and Mr. Frog are back again.

LESSON IV *PRODUCTION*

[MATERIALS]   **Mr. Frog, Mr. Pig, Listening Ears, and a toy boat.**

REVIEW

Put on your Listening Ears. Mr. Frog and Mr. Pig want to see how well you hear and how well you remember. What did we do with the pictures yesterday?

ACTIVITY

I'm going to tell you the story of a boat,[2] which goes *putt-putt-putt*. Can you do that—*putt-putt-putt*? You can help me tell the story by saying *putt, putt, putt* when I give you the signal.

On a fall afternoon a strange noise could be heard down by the river— *putt, putt, putt*. Far away a little boat could be seen. As it came closer, the *putt, putt, putt* became louder. The boys and girls standing by the river were so surprised to see such a little boat making such a loud *putt, putt* sound. The little boat puffed *putt, putt, putt,* much louder when he saw all the boys and girls. He was so proud of his *putt, putt, putt,* that he didn't notice a big log floating down the river. The *putt, putt, putt* became very loud. Then crash! The boat hit the log. All the boys and girls could only watch as the little boat went *putt, putt, putt, putt, putt, blub, blub,* as it sank to the bottom of the river.

How many of you have seen boats at the lake? On the river? Do any of your fathers have boats? We'll pretend we're going to take a boat trip now and we'll be thinking of things we'd like to take on our boat trip. We'll have to load it with supplies, and we'll have everyone tell us one thing he would like to put on the boat. I'll start by putting some milk on the boat. (**Have the child use the phrase, "I'll put _____ on our boat."**)

---

[2] Adapted from *The River Boat* in the *p* section of *My Speech Book*, Public Schools, Kansas City, Missouri, 1952.

We have so much on the boat it might sink! But it's fun getting ready for a boat trip.

Did anyone think of bringing popcorn for the boat trip? What would we need to pop corn? (**A pan**) Would you like to pretend that you are the little kernels that pop into popcorn? I'll say a little rhyme for you about popping corn, and you do the actions that go with it. All of you stand up.

I'm a piece of popcorn.
Put me in a pan.   (**Children step forward and squat**)
Shake me and shake me   (**They shake themselves**)
As fast as you can
And I'll pop!   (**They pop up**)

Tomorrow we'll bring something for sharing time. Till then we'll put the Listening Ears back in the Sound Box.

LESSON V *SHARING TIME*

REVIEW

Are we ready to bring out our Sound Box, with Mr. Frog, Mr. Pig, and our Listening Ears? Who remembers what sound the little boat made on the river? What happened to the kernels of corn as we shook them?

ACTIVITY

As we show our things, wouldn't it be fun to begin by saying, "Mr. Pig and Mr. Frog, I brought _____." Mr. Pig will be leaving us for a while after today.

(**After sharing time is concluded, tell the children Mr. Frog has another surprise for them for the next day.**)

[ADDITIONAL ACTIVITIES FOR THIS UNIT]
1. Have the children draw a pig or color one. Have them tell about an experience they've had with pigs.
2. During music time—sing the song "Pop Goes the Weasel."
3. Begin the scrap book. Ask the children to bring pictures with the *p* sound in their names, and give them an opportunity to show their pictures to the class before they are pasted in the scrap book.
4. Check Appendixes B and C for additional stories for Unit 2.
5. During physical education—play Piggy in the Pen. Children hold hands in a circle, with the pig in the center. The Pig tries to escape as the children chant, "Pig is in the pen and he can't get out." He must not go over or under the locked hands, but has to break through them. When he does, the children cry, "Pig is out." He then picks a child to be the next pig.

UNIT 3

k Sound–Captain Kangaroo

LESSON I *IDENTIFICATION*

[MATERIALS]   Mr. Frog, Listening Ears, a picture of Captain Kangaroo, mirrors, and a red paper tongue.

ACTIVITIES

Mr. Frog has a new friend for you to meet, a friend that some of you have seen on television or read about. He wears a uniform and carries keys. He knows Mr. Green Jeans. Yes, it is Captain Kangaroo. We will put his picture where we can see it.

Captain Kangaroo told Mr. Frog a poem about himself, that I think you'd like to hear.

> "k-k-k," says Captain Kangaroo,
> "My name has the 'k' sound."
> "k-k-k," says Captain Kangaroo,
> "Does your name have that sound too?"

We'll say the poem together. How many of your names have the *k* sound? Let's ask the boys first. (**Ken, Chris, Carl, Keith, Calvin**) What about you girls? (**Carol, Christine, Cora, Carolyn, Candy, Kitty**) Do any of you have last names that have Captain Kangaroo's sound?

How do we make the *k* sound? Can you feel the back of your tongue touching the roof of your mouth? (**Demonstrate with the red tongue, using the palm of your hand for the roof of the mouth.**) Watch your neighbor as he makes the *k* sound. Look in your mirror as you make the sound.

Let's tell Captain Kangaroo *hello* all together. "Hello, Captain Kangaroo." Can you hear the *k* sound? That is Captain Kangaroo's sound and it is the one we will be talking about this week. There are also some birds and animals that make the *k* sound. Can you think of some? (**Crow, caw, caw, caw; cuckoo in the clock, coo, coo; chicken, cutt-cutt, cluck-cluck, or cock-a-doodle-doo**)

If you think very hard you can think of some colors that have the *k* sound. (**If necessary show crayons to children.**) Can you think of some? (**Black and pink**)

Let's say Captain Kangaroo's poem together again and all the children whose names have Captain Kangaroo's sound can stand up.

Tomorrow we'll hear a story about Captain Kangaroo.

LESSON II *LISTENING*

[MATERIALS]   Any of the Captain Kangaroo stories, published as Little Golden Books, can be used for the listening session. Kathleen N. Daly, *Captain Kangaroo and the Panda*, New York, Golden Press, is recommended.

REVIEW

Do you remember who Mr. Frog brought to see us yesterday? Captain Kangaroo. What is his sound? (*k-k-k*)

ACTIVITIES

(If you tell the recommended story, use the name *Koko* for the panda bear and wherever possible in the story insert the phrase, "Koko said, *k-k-k-k*." The children can help to tell the story by making the Captain Kangaroo sound when you signal. The *k* sound is the only one Koko bear knows how to make.)

The following questions can be asked of the children if you tell this story. If you use another one, ask them questions about the story.
1. What did Captain Green Jeans bring to Captain Kangaroo?
2. What did Koko say?
3. What did Captain Kangaroo ride up the mountain?
4. What sat on Koko's shoulder?
5. What story did Koko tell his pals?

Tomorrow we'll play a game with Captain Kangaroo. Shall we say good-bye to the Captain and the panda bear, Koko?

LESSON III *DISCRIMINATION*

[MATERIALS]   Mr. Frog, Captain Kangaroo, Listening Ears, and pictures.

REVIEW

What sound are we learning about this week? (*k-k-k*) Who makes this sound? (**Captain Kangaroo and Koko bear**)

ACTIVITIES

1. Pretend I'm Koko bear. Clap when you hear me make Captain Kangaroo's sound: *r-r-r, s-s-s, k-k-k, f-f-f, sh-sh-sh, t-t-t, g-g-g, k-k-k*.
2. Sometimes people use Captain Kangaroo's sound when they need it. At other times they don't. Clap when I use the sound correctly and we'll talk about what I say wrong.

a. Can you catch it?
b. Yes, I tan.
c. I want a tooky.
d. Do you like tandy?
e. I like cake.

3. Do you notice anything different about Captain Kangaroo's uniform? Yes, it has very large pockets. Do real kangaroos have pockets? (**Discuss this briefly if desired.**) We will use Captain Kangaroo's pockets for a game we are going to play. Name these pictures (**use pictures listed below**) and if the name of the picture contains Captain Kangaroo's sound, we'll put it in his pocket. If not, we'll put it in a pile near Mr. Frog.

THOSE WITH *k*		THOSE WITHOUT *k*	
cow-46	cup-55	tree-5	gate
pancakes-47	doctor-56	shirt-19	potatoes
ink-48	taxicab-57	elephant-65	table
key-49	coats-58	girls-82	tie
bacon-50	monkeys-59	wagon-86	tiger
tractor-51	squirrel-60	train-130	top
candy-52	truck-61		
turkey-53	cat-62		
basket-54	clock-63		

Let's take the pictures from Captain Kangaroo's pocket and name them together. Tomorrow we will have some new games to play with Captain Kangaroo's sound.

LESSON IV *PRODUCTION*

[MATERIALS]   **Pictures used in the preceding lesson, and Captain Kangaroo.**

REVIEW

Can you name the television friend we met this week? (**Captain Kangaroo**) What special sound do we hear in his name? (***k-k-k***)

ACTIVITIES

1. Captain Kangaroo has a song for us to learn. The tune of the song is *Mary Had a Little Lamb.*

> Once there was a kangaroo, kangaroo, kangaroo,
> Once there was a kangaroo, and he said, "*K-k-k.*"

Can you jump like kangaroos while you sing the song?
2. (**Play a game with this song. One child is chosen to be the leader. He**

is the kangaroo. The kangaroo chooses one of the *k* pictures used in the preceding lesson and shows it to the other children. They hide their eyes and sing the song as the kangaroo hides the picture, or as the teacher hides it. Then the children take turns guessing where the picture is. They say, "I think the _____ is _____." The child who guesses becomes the new kangaroo. The game may be played a number of times.)

You should carry something to school tomorrow that you would like to show to Captain Kangaroo.

LESSON V *SHARING TIME*

REVIEW

Can you remember your television friend? (**Captain Kangaroo**) What is his sound? (*k-k-k*)

ACTIVITY

(Each child is given an opportunity to show the class and Captain Kangaroo what he has carried to school. He should use the phrase, "I carried my _____ to school," or a similar phrase telling what he carried it in: car, bicycle basket, etc. If the children wish, they may tell why they especially desired to show this object to Captain Kangaroo.)

Mr. Frog will bring us another friend tomorrow.

[ADDITIONAL ACTIVITIES FOR THIS UNIT]
1. During singing time—sing the Kangaroo song.
2. During physical education time—play the Kangaroo game.
3. During free time—place the Captain Kangaroo book where the children can examine it.
4. During story time—read some of the stories suggested in Appendix B for Unit 3.
5. In the first grade—talk about the Captain Kangaroo sound in new reading words, particularly in action words like *can, carry, come.*
6. Other activities:
a. Talk about things we eat that have the *k* sound: corn, carrots, candy, cake, cookies, cabbage, milk, etc.
b. During unit on farm discuss animals whose names have the *k* sound: cat, kitten, cow, chicken, turkey, duck; and animals that make the *k* sound in what they say: pig, oink: chicken, cluck, cock-a-doodle-doo, cut-cut; duck, quack.
c. Play a game using a fishing pole and magnet. The child should say, "I caught a _____."

UNIT 4

s Sound–Teakettle

LESSON I *IDENTIFICATION*

[MATERIALS]   **Mr. Frog, Listening Ears, a teakettle, and mirrors.**

ACTIVITIES

Last week Mr. Frog brought his friend Captain Kangaroo to visit us. What surprise do you think he has in his box today? It's something mother uses in the kitchen, on the stove, to boil water. Yes, it's a teakettle. When the water steams out of the teakettle, what does it say? *s - - -, s - - -, s - - -*. If the water boils over onto the stove, the *s - - -* becomes even louder. Do you suppose Captain Kangaroo might have needed a kettle for fixing Koko's dinner?

Let's pass out our mirrors now, so that everyone can see how he makes the teakettle sound. Our front teeth are almost touching. We don't let our tongues slip between the teeth. Try it: *s-s-s*. (**Check the children to see if they are following your directions.**) Put your finger in front of your lips, but not touching them, and feel the air come out between your teeth when you say *s*.

The teakettle sound appears in lots of our names. Which of you girls have names with the *s* sound? (**Sally, Susan, Sandy, Stella, Sylvia, Jessie, Janice, Grace, Leslie, Doris, Denise, Cecelia, Lucy, Esther**) Are there any boys whose names have the *s* sound? (**Stephen, Sam, Sidney, Stanley, Ross, Oscar, Lawrence, Chris**) Do any of you have the *s* sound in your last names?

Many things with which we play have the teakettle sound in them. What's on the playground that has the *s* on it? (**Swing, see-saw**) What happens when two of you get on the slippery slide? Would you like to learn a rhyme about a slippery slide? Pick partners and slide with the poem.

> A slippery slide is lots of fun,
> It makes us laugh as we go down,
> Then up we bounce as Susy slips,
> And down she comes to end her trips.

The holiday we will have soon has the *s* sound in its name. What is it? Thanksgiving! Tomorrow I'll be telling you a story about Thanksgiving. We'll put away our Sound Box with Mr. Frog, our Listening Ears, and our teakettle.

LESSON II *LISTENING*

Yesterday Mr. Frog brought us something new. What was it? What sound did it make? Do you know what days of the week have the *s* sound in them? Listen to the names, and raise your hands when you hear one, or clap your hands. (**Saturday, Sunday**) What holidays have the teakettle sound? (**Thanksgiving, Christmas [has 2 of them], Easter**)

I want you to listen for all the teakettle sounds in the story I'm going to tell you. It's about Sally and Stephen who spent Thanksgiving with their grandmother.

A TRIP TO GRANDMOTHER'S HOUSE

When school was out on Wednesday, Sally and Stephen hurried home to see if Daddy and Mother were ready to leave for Grandmother's house in the far off city. They had to leave before supper, so that they would arrive at Grandmother's before midnight. It would be past Sally's and Stephen's usual bed-time when they got there; but since they didn't have to go to school the next day, they could sleep as late as they wanted.

The car was packed when they got home from school, so that all they had to do was to change their clothes. Sally put on a heavy skirt and sweater, just in case it got cold; and Stephen decided to put his boots in the car, too. Because they would have late supper at Grandma's they just had some soup and sandwiches.

When they finally got started, Daddy noticed that some light flakes of snow were falling. Everyone hoped the snow would stop, because the roads might become slick and Grandmother would worry about them. As they drove further, the sun began to set, it got dark, and the snow fell faster and faster. The lights from the car made the snow look almost like stars. Stephen and Sally watched it and were so happy, because it meant they could finally use the sleds they had left at Grandma's house. Daddy drove slowly because he didn't want to have an accident. For a while it was hard to see the road, because of the falling snow. Mother worried about how late it would be when they arrived at Grandma's. Once Daddy took a wrong road, and had to ask a policeman for directions. The falling snow made Sally sleepy; so she curled up in the back seat of the car, and went sound asleep.

Stephen didn't know what to do with himself. He couldn't read his books, because it was too dark. He couldn't talk to Sally because she had gone to sleep. Mother was helping Daddy to keep on the right road. He decided to sing some of the songs he had learned in school. But his singing bothered Daddy who was getting tired of driving into the snow. Then he decided he was hungry; and because he complained about it so much, Daddy finally stopped and bought him an ice cream cone. Sally still slept in the back seat. After a while Stephen too dozed. His head dropped, and he had trouble keeping his eyes open. Mother suggested that he curl up like Sally. She promised to awaken him when they arrived at Grandmother's house.

It was long past midnight when Daddy pulled into Grandma's driveway. The lights were burning brightly though, because Grandma was waiting for them to arrive. As Daddy stopped the car, she hurried out in the snow to greet them. She helped Sally and Stephen to wake up; and with Daddy's help, she got them into the house. Mother brought in the small suitcases, and Daddy carried in the big one.

Sally and Stephen were still so sleepy that they didn't want any supper. So, they undressed with Grandma's help, and soon were in bed.

Because it was so late, Grandma had taken the teakettle off the stove many hours before. Now she put it on again, so she, Daddy, and Mother could have some hot tea before they went to bed. Daddy told Grandma about the snow, and how slick the roads became. As he talked, the teakettle began to boil. It went *s - - -, s - - -.* (**Have the children do it too.**) She hurried to take it from the stove.

Finally tea was ready. Mother helped to get the cups and saucers out of the cupboard for Grandma. Just as they sat down to drink their tea, Grandmother suddenly remembered that it was already Thanksgiving Day. They wished one another a Happy Thanksgiving, and Daddy kissed Grandmother and Mother again. Soon they tiptoed into the bedrooms where Sally and Stephen were already in dreamland. They tiptoed away. Soon they too were sleeping. They knew they had many things for which to be thankful, and particularly for being able to celebrate Thanksgiving as always with Grandmother.

(**Discussion following the story can be directed into many channels. The children might take the parts of the five people in the story, and re-create it. They might retell the story in their own words. Or they might be questioned about the story. Following is a list of questions that require responses with the *s* sound. Encourage the children to reply in complete sentences.**)

1. What were the names of the boy and girl in the story?
2. What did they eat before leaving for grandmother's house?
3. What kind of weather did they have?
4. What did Sally do after it got dark?
5. What did Stephen do?
6. What did his father buy him when he said he was hungry?
7. What did Grandma use to boil water for the tea?
8. What sound did it make as it started to boil?
9. What did Grandma remember as they started to drink their tea?

LESSON III *DISCRIMINATION*

[MATERIALS]   **Listening Ears, Mr. Frog, and a teakettle.**

REVIEW

What sound came from the singing teakettle? Can you make it loud? Soft?

ACTIVITIES

We know many things that have the *s* sound in them. Let's first of all talk about some foods we eat. What do we eat that has this sound? (**Cereal, soup, sandwiches, sardines, cakes, nuts, ice cream, spinach, squash**) What do we eat that doesn't have this sound? (**Meat, potatoes, bread, milk, candy, beans, eggs, cheese**)

When we eat, we use some things besides our fingers. What are they? (**Forks, knives, spoons, dishes, plates, cups, saucers, glasses, bowls**) Which of these have our teakettle sound in them?

Many of our clothes have the *s* sound in them. Which ones can you think of? (**Dress, sweater, skirt, socks, coats, suit, snowshoes, bedroom slippers**) Which ones don't? (**Shirt, shoe, pajamas, bathrobe**)

Many of our numbers have the teakettle sound. Raise your hands when I say one that has it; shake your head when I say one that doesn't. (**6, 7, 16, 26, 60. Mix up the numbers as you present them to the children.**)

Do you remember how we played see-saw last week? Each one took a partner, and the see-saw went up and down. Each of you pick a partner now, and we'll form a circle, but we'll have the partners join hands. I'm going to stand in the middle of the circle, and I'm going to say some funny pairs of words. If the words are really partners, they'll *both* have the teakettle sound in them. If they do, then *both* ends of the see-saw will go down. We'll try one for practice:

sun—bun	(**Both sides stay up**)
stand—sit	(**Both sides go down**)

Listen carefully.

sat—fat	shirt—skirt	this—that
sun—soon	scrap—scratch	paste—waist
sheet—seat	scramble—scribble	sister—mister
sing—thing	salt—pepper	yes—no
think—sink	Sally—Susan	September—December
school—skate	sign—sigh	ship—skip

When Mr. Frog comes back tomorrow, what do you suppose he'll want us to do?

LESSON IV *DISCRIMINATION*

[MATERIALS]   **Mr. Frog, teakettle, Listening Ears, and pictures.**

REVIEW

Our sound is the teakettle sound—*s-s-s-s*. Who can remember some things we talked about yesterday that have our sound in them?

ACTIVITIES

All of us will try a rhyme about a teapot. (**Go over the words with the children before adding the actions.**) As we say the lines, we'll do the actions with them.

I'm a little teapot, short and stout	(**Children squat**)
Here is my handle, here is my spout.	(**Arms form handle and spout**)
When you look me over I just shout	
Tip me over and pour me out.	(**Tip spout arm down**)
S-S-S-S-S-S-S-S.	

While we are in a circle, I'm going to give each of you a card with a picture. Look at the picture; and if its name has the *s* sound in it, you stay standing in the circle. All the others will sit down in the circle. (**Where this latter direction is not feasible, have them return to their seats.**) Those standing in the circle will take turns telling us the names of their pictures. Each one will say, "This is a picture of _____." Of course, if his picture doesn't have the teakettle sound in it, we'll tell him. Then, all the boys and girls who have pictures without the *s* sound in their names, will show us their pictures and tell us what they are. (**Again have them use the carrier phrase, "This is a picture of _____."**)

PICTURES WITH *s*		PICTURES WITHOUT *s*	
sailor-1	swing-10	shirt-19	dishes
pencil-2	scouts-11	brush-24	thumb
horse-3	school-12	shoe-25	roof
soup-4	spider web-13	knife-35	
spoon-4	strawberries-14	telephone-68	
Christmas tree-5	swimming-15	fruit-78	
house-6	ice skating-16	frog-84	
sink-7	desk-17	thimble-100	
policeman-8	sled-18	radish-118	
circus-9			

Mr. Frog would like to have all of you smile for him. Turn to the person on your right, and say:

Smile with me,
It's fun, you see.

LESSON V *PRODUCTION*

[MATERIALS]   **Pictures from previous day.**

ACTIVITIES

In our Sound Box we have many pictures. We're going to try to guess the name of the picture from the clues we get. I'll start by pulling a card from the Sound Box, and giving you some hints about what it is. When you think you know, raise your hands and I'll call you. Whoever gives the right answer will then have a turn. He'll draw a picture and give us clues; then he'll ask someone to tell him the name of his picture. (**Use the pictures from the previous day.**)

LESSON VI *SHARING TIME*

(**During this period have the children use the carrier phrase, "I brought _____ to school."**)

[ADDITIONAL ACTIVITIES FOR THIS UNIT]
1. A unit on safety—school safety, street safety.
2. Select some stories, like those suggested in Appendix B, Unit 4, for story time.
3. A science lesson, utilizing a teakettle and a hot-plate, for production of steam.
4. A unit on the circus, if the timing is appropriate.
5. Make or color teakettles in an art lesson.
6. Show the movie, *Little Black Sambo,* and dramatize the story.

UNIT 5

z Sound—Buzzing Bee

LESSON I *INTRODUCTION*

[MATERIALS]   Mr. Frog, Buzzing Bee, and mirrors.

ACTIVITIES

Last week we learned about the sound made by the teakettle. Our new sound is very much like the *s* sound. It's made the same way, except for one thing. For *s*, the motor in the voice box is turned off; for *z* it's turned on. Feel the motor with your fingers on your throat as you say *zzz*.

Mr. Frog has brought Buzzing Bee along with him today to help us to learn about the new sound. Can you hear the sound in his name? Buzzing Bee. (**Overemphasize the *z*.**) Look in your mirror and check to make sure your tongue is behind your teeth.

What days of the week have the *z* sound in them? (**Tuesday, Wednesday, Thursday**)

Do we have anyone whose name has the Buzzing Bee sound in it? (**Louise, Elizabeth, Josephine and Joseph, Rose, Rosemary, Susan, both *s* and *z*; Ambrose, Francis, also both *s* and *z***)

Many parts of our bodies have the Buzzing Bee sound in their names. Can you think of some of them? (**Ears, eyes, nose, arms, legs, fingers, toes**) What do we put on our fingers when it's cold? (**Mittens or gloves**) On our feet? (**Shoes**) To see better what do we wear? (**Glasses**) When a button falls off, what does Mother sometimes use? (**Pins**) What things do we use in our room that has the *z* sound in their names? (**Pencils, crayons, mirrors, music, dolls, signs**)

Tomorrow Buzzing Bee will take us on a trip.

LESSON II *LISTENING*

Mr. Frog and Buzzing Bee are ready for our story. Are you? What sound will you listen for in particular? *zzz*. As Buzzing Bee tells his story you will help him by making the *zzz* sound when I tell you.

Buzzing Bee was very excited. You see he usually spent his time going *zzzzzz* around the flowers gathering pollen. This pollen he carried back to the beehive where it was made into honey for all the other bees to eat. But today he had a very special job. Mr. Frog had asked him to gather some things which had the *zz* sound. Mr. Frog was very busy and he needed some things having the *zz* sound to show to kindergarten boys and girls.

Zzzzzz, off flew Buzzing Bee to begin his search. He was so used to flying around the flowers that a flowerbed was the first place that he stopped. Here were zinnias and daisies, pansies and roses. Buzzing Bee was so surprised when he realized that all these flowers had his sound that he didn't know what to do. Zinnias, daisies, pansies, and roses! He couldn't take all the flowers; but after thinking a minute, he chose a daisy and some roses. Mr. Frog would like these things which had the *zzz* sound.

"I'm going to have to hurry," Buzzing Bee thought. He flew across the street and over to the zoo. And what do you suppose were the first animals he saw there? You're right, he saw the zebras. Down buzzed the bee. "Mr. Zebra," he shouted, "I need your help." The zebra hurried over. Buzzing Bee explained that he was looking for things with a *zzzz* sound because Mr. Frog had asked him to help. Mr. Zebra said, "That's how my name begins. May I come with you?"

Zelda's mother was sitting on her porch doing some mending when— could she believe her eyes! Here came a zebra and a buzzing bee down the street. Mother was so excited that she spilled her sewing basket as she ran inside to find Zelda. Mr. Zebra and Buzzing Bee stopped in front of her porch. "Look, Mr. Zebra, there is a pair of scissors." Mr. Zebra was pawing around among the things which had spilled from the sewing basket. "And here is a zipper," he said.

"Zelda's mother won't care if we borrow these to show the children," Buzzing Bee told Mr. Zebra. "Would you carry the zipper and scissors?" And off they went to continue their search. Soon Zelda and her mother came outside again. They couldn't see the buzzing bee or the zebra and, do you know, they couldn't find a zipper or Mother's scissors!

As the zebra and the buzzing bee traveled along, Mr. Zebra said, "I'm very hungry. Do you suppose we could stop somewhere long enough for me to get something to eat?" So the next time they came to a drugstore in went Mr. Zebra and Buzzing Bee. The druggist was very surprised to see a zebra and a buzzing bee in his store, but he asked them what they wanted. "Do you have any candybars?" asked Mr. Zebra.

"Y-y-y-yes," replied the druggist as he handed the zebra two candybars. Mr. Zebra turned to leave but *zzzzzz*, Buzzing Bee was flying in circles above his head.

Suddenly Mr. Zebra understood. He turned again to the druggist. "May I please have two more candybars?" That's right. He needed candybars because they have the *zzzzz* sound. He wanted to take them to Mr. Frog.

As they went down the street Buzzing Bee and Mr. Zebra met some boys and girls. The boys and girls weren't used to seeing a zebra and a buzzing bee on the street, so these two had to explain why they were there. One boy asked, "Why not take some boys and girls with you?"

"That's a good idea," Mr. Zebra and Buzzing Bee said at the same time. Why did they take boys and girls with them? Yes, boys and girls have the *zzzz* sound. The boys and girls could help Mr. Frog.

Time for the search had ended. Mr. Frog was waiting outside his house when he saw a strange sight coming toward him. First flew Buzzing Bee carrying a daisy and some roses. Mr. Zebra loped along next. He was carrying a pair of scissors, a zipper, and two candybars, in his teeth. And behind Buzzing Bee and Mr. Zebra were many boys and girls.

Mr. Frog said, "Thank you, Buzzing Bee. Thank you, Mr. Zebra. Thank you, boys and girls, for helping me fill my Sound Box with things that have the *zzzz* sound."

Can you think of any other objects Buzzing Bee might have brought back with him that have the *zzzz* sound? (**Dogs, hens, chickens**)

ACTIVITIES

Do you remember what Buzzing Bee brought back with him?

We have a rhyme that we must learn before we can use it to play a game in the circle. It goes like this:

> Buzz, buzz, buzz, went the doorbell,
> Th, th, th, went the plane (**As in this**)
> Zip, zip, zip, went the zipper,
> Stop, called the bee, I'm in pain.

Who will be our first Buzzing Bee? He'll stand in the middle, and all the rest will form a circle. He'll close his eyes. All of us will say the rhyme until we get to the word *stop*. Then the circle will stop, and Buzzing Bee will point to someone. Whoever it is will then be the next Buzzing Bee.

LESSON III *DISCRIMINATION*

[MATERIALS]   **Red and green slips of paper, a purse, and pictures for this lesson.**

REVIEW

Whom did Buzzing Bee bring back from the Zoo? What else had he collected? Is the motor in the voice box on or off when we say *zzzz?*

ACTIVITIES

Each of you has two pieces of colored paper, one red and one green. We're going to play the game, Mr. Frog Says. If he says something that requires us to use our motors, then we'll hold up the green paper. Otherwise, we'll hold up the red one.

Mr. Frog Says:	Touch your nose
	Wiggle all over
	Cheese!
	Pick up sticks
	Ring around the rosy
	Play games
	Hide your eyes
	Listen
	Eat your breakfast
	Come in
	Three pigs
	Pick a daisy
	Sing a song
	Today is Wednesday
	Goodbye

We have several objects in our Sound Box, some of which we could put in a purse; some we wouldn't. Who will hold our purse? Who wants to pull out the first object? When you do, you'll tell us it *does* or *doesn't* go in the purse. If it does, put it in.

THOSE THAT DO	THOSE THAT DON'T
gloves-39	football-67
kleenex	wagon-86
pennies	vase-157
glasses	orange

(**Remove the pictures or objects from the purse and ask the children which one [kleenex] doesn't have the Buzzing Bee sound.**)

Our purse has a zipper on it. What other things do we have that use zippers? (**Encourage the children to reply in sentences such as: "Dresses have zippers."**)

LESSON IV *DISCRIMINATION AND PRODUCTION*

[MATERIALS]   An easel, art paper, crayons, pictures, and paste.

REVIEW

Who is in the Sound Box? What does he say? Where does he buzz?

ACTIVITY

Newspapers tell us about many events. We'll plan what stories we could put into our own newspaper, and perhaps some of you can draw or color something for our paper. (**Place a large sheet of art paper on an easel. Ask** the children to tell you what they want in their newspaper. Someone might draw the sun shining; another, a school with a play area. Others could select some pictures of activities that they want in the paper, like the policeman helping the children to cross the street, the bus that brings the children to school, the animals in the stories they have read, a birthday cake for someone's party. When the children indicate what they would like to see in their paper, encourage them to use the carrier phrase, "In our newspaper I'd put _____.")

LESSON V *SHARING TIME*

During this period use the carrier phrase, "This is a _____."

[ADDITIONAL ACTIVITIES FOR THIS UNIT]
1. Stories about the zoo, or bees, or those suggested in Appendix B, Unit 5.
2. Physical activities in which the children demonstrate how the animals walk.

UNIT 6

Review of *p*, *k*, *s*, and *z*

LESSON I *IDENTIFICATION*

(This unit will come during the month of December, if the class has started its speech improvement program in October or early November. However, if a different sequence is followed by the teacher, the use of Christmas stockings and songs can be eliminated, and the ideas modified in order to carry out the activities.)

[MATERIALS]   Mr. Frog, Mr. Pig, Captain Kangaroo, Tommy Teakettle, Buzzing Bee, and mirrors.

ACTIVITIES

Very soon Christmas will be here. At Christmas time family and friends get together to celebrate the holiday. Do you do anything special at your house? Does Grandmother come for the day? Do you visit your aunts and uncles and cousins? (**Discussion of Christmas and Santa Claus can continue if the teacher wishes.**)

Mr. Frog has invited his four friends to return and stay with us all week. Do you remember the first one to whom he introduced us? The one who lives on the farm and has two brothers? He says "oink, oink." (**Give additional clues that may be needed until the children guess the pig.**) We'll take him from our Sound Box, and put him beside Mr. Frog. Who remembers the names of the three pigs? (**Peter, Paul, Pat**) When the wolf came to blow down the houses, what did he do? He puffed and puffed till *all* the houses blew down? No, Peter's house stayed up. Let's have all of you go *p, p, p,* as you pretend you are blowing down the houses.

Who can guess the name of the second visitor that Mr. Frog has brought back? He's the one we watch on television—he took the Panda Bear named Koko to find bamboo shoots. Captain Kangaroo! What is the only sound that Koko could make? (*k-k-k-k*) Let's do it together.

Our next visitor was the one whom we met near Thanksgiving time. The teakettle, which made the *s-s-s-s* sound.

And which one did we meet last week? Buzzing Bee, who made the *z* sound. Who was the little girl in the story? What things did Buzzing Bee bring back to Mr. Frog?

Now that we have our visitors, let's see if we can look in our mirrors and see how we make the sounds which they told us about. (**The teacher will ask the children to make each sound in isolation as they watch their mouths—*p, k, s, z*.**) What part of our faces do we use to make *p? k? s? z?* (**Lips for the *p*, back of tongue and roof of the mouth for *k*, teeth for *s*, and teeth and voice for *z*.**)

Let's have you listen and watch while I make the sounds, and then those of you who have names with that sound come up and stand beside the visitor. (**All those with *s, z, p, k,* in their names.**) Is everyone with the *s* sound in his name standing? (**All the children can help to identify any children who have made mistakes in associating their names with the special sound.**)

Who can tell me which of our sounds are found in Santa? Santa *C*laus? *C*hristmas? Hap*py* New Year? *C*andy *C*anes? (**Overemphasize any of the four sounds as they appear in the words.**)

Tomorrow we'll have the same visitors with us. They'll be inviting us to do some other things with them then.

LESSON II *DISCRIMINATION*

[MATERIALS]   **Mr. Frog, Mr. Pig, Captain Kangaroo, Tommy Teakettle, and Buzzing Bee.**

ACTIVITIES

1. Who can tell me the names of our visitors today? Can you make their sounds? Captain Kangaroo's friend Koko says? (***k-k-k***) Tommy Teakettle? (***s-s-s***) Mr. Pig starts with? (***p***) And Buzzing Bee goes? (***zzz***) Two of these sounds are made with the teeth almost together, and the tongue behind them. Which two are they? (***s* and *z***)

2. We're going to play a game in which you will help me to decide which of these two sounds are in the names I tell you. What about Santa? Santa Claus? Tuesday, music, Snowman? (**Add the names of any children whose names have these two sounds.**)

3. Sometimes we have words that have both of these sounds in them—both *s* and *z*. I can think of *s*ci*ss*ors, S-u*s*an, voi*ces*, dre*sses*. (**See if the children can add to this list. Suggest that they think of toys, or names, or objects in the room.**)

4. Our visitors have some riddles for you. When you know the answer to the riddle, raise your hand; and when I call on you, tell all of us the answers. (**Encourage the children to use sentences.**)

  a. When it's cold outside, what do we put on our feet to play on the lake when it's frozen? (**Ice skates, overshoes, heavy socks**)

  b. When do we swim in the lake? (**Summer**)

  c. What goes with pepper? (**Salt**)

d. What day comes after Tuesday? (**Wednesday**)
e. What month is this one? (**December**)
f. What part of our body helps us see? (**Eyes**)
g. What do we use for smelling? (**Nose**)
h. What do we wear on our feet? (**Shoes, socks**)
 i. What helps us to hear? (**Ears**)
 j. When we go to bed and the lights are out, what are we to do? (**Sleep**)

5. All of you are going to get into a circle in a moment; I'll tell you when to start walking (**or skipping**). When you hear a word that has either the *s* or *z* sound in it, everyone stops. Then you'll tell me the word and whose sound it has in it. We'll start with an easy nursery rhyme.

> Pussy-cat, pussy-cat, where have you been?
> "I've been to London to see the queen."
> Pussy-cat, pussy-cat, what did you do there?
> "I frightened a little mouse under the chair."

6. Now this time we'll sing the song, "Jingle Bells," and when we come to the words with the *s* and *z* sounds, we'll stop walking but not singing and then I'll clap my hands when you are to start walking again.

> Jingle bells, jingle bells,
> Jingle all the way
> Oh what fun it is to ride
> On a one-horse open sleigh.

Shall we try that one again?
We'll sit down now, and invite our friends to come back tomorrow.

LESSON III *DISCRIMINATION AND PRODUCTION*

[MATERIALS]   **Four Christmas stockings and pictures.**

ACTIVITIES

1. Mr. Frog decided this morning that his four visitors should take a trip to toyland. While they're gone, he thought it would be fun if we filled a Christmas stocking for each one of them. How many of you had Christmas stockings last year? What did you find on Christmas morning in your stockings?

Which of you would like to hold the Christmas stocking for Mr. Pig? For Captain Kangaroo? Tommy Teakettle? Buzzing Bee? (**To make it easier for the children to remember which stocking belongs to each of the four, you might pin on the children who are holding the stockings a picture of the characters that had been drawn or colored during the weeks in which the specific sound had been introduced.**)

Before you drop your picture in the stocking, tell the class what it is, as you show us; and as you place it in the stocking tell the one to whom you're giving the picture: "Happy Christmas Mr. Pig, or Tommy Teakettle."

List of pictures that children will put into the four stockings:

CAPTAIN KANGAROO	MR. PIG	TOMMY TEAKETTLE	BUZZING BEE
key-49	plane-37	suit-1	shoes-25
truck-51	penny	horse-3	bees-162
candy-52	paint	house-6	xylophone-166
turkey-53	potatoes	swing-10	easel-167
coat-58	top	strawberry-14	zebra-169
monkey-59	pear	sled-18	rose-171
cat-62			
clock-63			

2. I have some pictures that we could put into two stockings. Let's see if we can decide which ones should get these. (**Christmas, skates, desk, basket**)

LESSON IV *PRODUCTION*

[MATERIALS]   **Those from the preceding day.**

ACTIVITIES

1. Well, Mr. Frog tells me that they all had a good time yesterday at toyland. Mr. Kangaroo, Mr. Pig, Buzzing Bee, and Tommy Teakettle are all eager to find out what you put in their stockings yesterday. Because they won't be here on Christmas Day, they would like us to tell them what we put in each of their stockings now. Before we do that, however, we could sing them a song. What about "Santa Claus Is Coming to Town?"

2. I'm going to take out the things we put in Captain Kangaroo's Christmas stocking, and as I show him and you what it is, whoever gave it to him will come up, take the picture, and put it in front of Captain Kangaroo. As you do this, wish him: "Merry Christmas, Captain Kangaroo."

Who would like to take the things from Tommy Teakettle's stocking? You show us what we put in it, and then whoever had that present yesterday, take it and wish Tommy Teakettle a Merry Christmas.

Let's have someone else show us the pictures from Buzzing Bee's stocking. Then we'll do the same thing.

Now let's have all those who gave pictures to Mr. Pig yesterday stand up and together we'll say, "Merry Christmas, Mr. Pig, and Happy New Year."

Tomorrow we'll have our sharing time and we'll begin with one of our Christmas songs.

LESSON V *SHARING TIME*

Did you remember that today is sharing time? What song shall we sing first? (If the children don't care which song is selected, you might like to use the first verse of "Frosty the Snowman," which includes so many words with the four sounds.

It may be that instead of showing something, you will want the children to tell what they want Santa to bring them. If you do, suggest that each one begin by saying, "I hope Santa Claus brings me _____ for Christmas." Then each child can tell something about what he wants, why he wants it, and how it works, what he could do with it.)

We'll all say goodbye to our five visitors. Mr. Frog will be back soon, but the others won't return for a long time.

UNIT 7

g Sound–Grey Goose

LESSON I *IDENTIFICATION*

[MATERIALS]   Mr. Frog, Grey Goose, mirrors, and a red paper tongue.

ACTIVITIES

How many of you have ever seen a goose? How many of you have eaten roast goose for Thanksgiving dinner, or Christmas dinner? Where does the goose live? Would we find him in a pond now? What sound would he make if he tried to tell us something? (*g-g-g*) Let's *all* try now to make the Grey Goose sound. All the girls make the same sound, *g-g-g*. Boys, stand up and pretend you are the Grey Goose—*g-g-g*.

The Grey Goose sound is the one we'll be learning about this week. Let's see if we have any boys or girls whose names begin with this sound. Of course, the word *girl* starts with the Grey Goose sound. Does anyone have a name with this sound in it? (**Gertrude, Gordon, Greg, Gus, Gladys, Grace, Gloria, Gwen**) **If any children have names with the g sound, have them stand and tell the group, "My name is _____; and it has the Grey Goose sound."**

Do you know any animals that use the sound in their names? (**Pig, tiger, dog, frog, hog, goat**)

What colors do we know that have this sound? (**Grey, green, gold; use the appropriate crayons and make some marks on white paper for the children.**)

We make the g sound by using the back of our tongues, the roof of our mouths, and our voices. (**Demonstrate with the red tongue, with the back of the tongue touching the curved hand.**) Look in your mirror as you say, *g-g-g*. Let's have everyone try to make the Grey Goose sound now.

Tomorrow we'll have a story about Grey Goose.

LESSON II *LISTENING*

What does the Grey Goose say? (*g-g-g*) Listen for the Grey Goose sound in our story.

Now that Christmas was over, Mr. and Mrs. Grey Goose decided that they should begin making plans for their trip to the Green Garden in the south. It would be warm there, and the baby geese would be able to swim most of the day. Mother and Father Goose called together their neighbors and before long, all you could hear was the *g-g-g* of the geese as they discussed their trip. Mother Goose wanted to take with her all the children and animals from her Mother Goose book; but Father Goose was afraid they'd lose some of them along the way. Finally, Mother Goose began selecting whom she wanted along. "What about Goldilocks, Father Goose?" He replied, *"Ga-ga-ga."* "Could we take the three pigs?" He replied, *"Ga-ga-ga*—yes." "What about Billy Goat?" After he thought about it a minute, he replied, "Yes, *g-g-g* Billy Goat can go too."

So, Mother and Father Goose, the baby geese, and their friends, Goldilocks, the three pigs, and Billy Goat, set out for the Green Garden. It took a long time to get there, because the baby geese had to go so slowly. As they travelled, they kept up a chatter of *g-g-g* along the way.

Finally, all the geese and their friends arrived at the Green Garden. There they settled down in the brick house that the pigs built for them. Goldilocks became everyone's friend, and Billy Goat ran all of her errands. They stayed in the Green Garden all winter; and finally when spring came, they returned to their pond in the park. Goldilocks went back to her grandmother, Billy Goat returned to the farm, and the three pigs started building another brick house near the pond. As each one left Mother and Father Goose, they waved good-bye, and the geese said, *g-g-g* as they watched their friends leave them until the next winter, when they hoped they could all return to the Green Garden once more.

Questions Based on the Story

1. Where did the geese want to go? (**Green Garden**)
2. Why did they want to go there? (**To go swimming**)
3. Whom did Mother Goose bring on the trip? (**Some of the friends from her Mother Goose book: Goldilocks, the three pigs, and Billy Goat.**)
4. What did Father Goose say about bringing so many guests to the Green Garden? (*Ga-ga-ga*—**We'll lose them**)
5. How long did they stay at Green Garden? (**All winter**)
6. Where did Goldilocks go after her visit to Green Garden? (**Back to her Grandmother**)
7. What about Billy Goat? (**Returned to the farm**)
8. What did the three pigs do? (**Built another brick house**)

LESSON III   *DISCRIMINATON*

[MATERIALS]   **Mr. Frog, Grey Goose, and pictures.**

ACTIVITIES

1. With what sound is Mr. Frog helping us this week? Who can make it? **(Call on different individuals, then the group.)**

2. Can you tell me if I make the Grey Goose sound correctly? When I make it right, raise your hand. When I make some other sound, shake your head. Now listen carefully: *g-g-g, s-s-s, g-g-g, sh-sh-sh, p-p-p, g-g-g.*

3. **(For this next activity the girls will be the ganders, and the boys the geese.)** Each child should be given the opportunity to buy at the store. Let each one pick a picture from the box. Some of the pictures will have names with the *g* sound, and others will not. As each child goes to the storekeeper, who can be a child with good speech, he will say, "I want to get some _____. It has—or hasn't—the *g* sound in its name." Those that do will be placed in a box near the Grey Goose, and those without it will be put into one near Mr. Frog. Following is the list of pictures to be used.

THOSE WITH *g*		THOSE WITHOUT *g*	
egg-50	grapes-91	desk-17	radish-118
spaghetti-83	magnet-93	dress-33	ball
frog-84	glass-94	candy-52	bed
garbage can-85	grapefruit-95	duck-53	dishes
wagon-86	goose-96	doll-98	reindeer
gum-88	globe-97		
kangaroo-89	buggy-98		
dog-90			

4. **(Place some of the pictures either on a flannel board or against a book. Call on individual children to name them and indicate whether they belong to the Grey Goose or not.)**

LESSON IV *PRODUCTION*

ACTIVITIES

1. **(Teach the children the following nursery rhyme from Mother Goose. Emphasize the *g* sound when it appears.)**

> To market, to market, to buy a fat pig,
> Home again, home again, jiggety-jig;
> To market, to market, to buy a fat hog,
> Home again, home again, jiggety-jig;
> To market, to market, to buy a big gun,
> Home again, home again, market is done.

2. **(Divide the class into three groups, and have group I stand and say the first two lines; group II, the next two; and group III, the last two lines.)**

3. **(Ask individual children if they remember any of the words in the poem which have the *g* sound.)**

4. Guessing game. (**Encourage the children to answer in sentences.**)

a. Who says "oink, "oink,"? (**Pig**)

b. Who barks? (**Dog**)

c. What fruits come in bunches? (**Grapes, bananas**)

d. Where do we keep the car? (**Garage**)

e. When do we eat turkey? (**Thanksgiving, Christmas**) Which has the *g* sound? (**Thanksgiving**)

f. What animal has a pouch? (**Kangaroo**)

g. What food goes with bacon? (**Eggs**)

h. What do we like to chew? (**Gum**)

i. When the sun shines brightly, what do we wear to cover our eyes? (**Dark glasses**)

j. What do we take when we go hunting? (**Gun**)

LESSON V   *SHARING TIME*

(Each child is to bring one toy or a picture to class. When he tells the group about it, have him use the phrase, "I'm going to show you _____ _____." Then he can tell something about it. For those children who forget to bring one, have them tell the group, "I forgot to bring my _____ _____." Then they can tell about it.)

[RELATED ACTIVITIES FOR THIS UNIT]

1. During art—stress the colors which use the *g sound*. Have the children draw the goose and goat.
2. During physical education—ask how the goose walks. Have the children form a circle, and walk like the goose.
3. Play the game Goose and Gander. The gander hides behind the teacher's desk or in the corner. Three or four children, designated as geese, as they get close to the gander, say "*g-g-g*"; as they start making the sound, the gander chases them. If he catches a goose before the goose gets to his seat, the goose then becomes the gander, and a new group of geese is selected to continue the game.
4. During story time—read the suggested books for this unit.

UNIT 8

sh Sound

LESSON I *IDENTIFICATION*

[MATERIALS]   Mr. Frog, seashells, and mirrors.

ACTIVITIES

Last week Mr. Frog brought us the Grey Goose. Today he wants to show us something we find in the sand by the sea. We can put it up to our ears and listen to it sing. Can anyone guess what it might be? A seashell! The seashell has the quiet sound in its name—*sh*. It's the sound I make when I want all of you to be quiet. When baby is asleep at home, Mother says, "*Sh*, don't wake up the baby."

Watch what I do with my lips when I say *sh*. My teeth are almost together. Look in your mirrors, and see how you make the quiet sound. (**Check each child as he makes the sound, and note for yourself what he may be doing incorrectly. Some children may make the *s* sound, or the *th* in place of the *sh*. Show those children how to do it, or have a child demonstrate for the class.**)

Each week we find some children whose names have the sound that we are learning about. Do any of your names have the quiet sound? Those who do, stand up and tell us your name. (**Sheila, Shirley, Sharon, Shannon, Marcia**) Do we have anyone whose last name has the quiet sound in it?

If we went with mother to shop, what might she buy that has the quiet sound in its name? (**At the grocery store: fish, mushrooms, radishes, sugar. At the department store: a washing machine, shoes, shirt, shovel, dishes, brushes, cushions. If the children are having difficulty thinking of some of these items, give them some clues, such as, something to wear on our feet, something to put food on.**)

Tomorrow we'll hear a story with our new sound in its name.

LESSON II *LISTENING*

What is our sound this week? Shall we put on our Listening Ears, so that we can listen for all the words in our story that have the quiet sound?

The story that is recommended for today's listening session is Louise B. Scott and J. J. Thompson, "The Seashell," from *Talking Time* (St. Louis, Mo., Webster Publishing Co., 1951). Any other stories which permit the

children to hear the *sh* sound and respond on cue with this sound can be utilized. At the end of the story ask the children questions requiring responses with the *sh* sound.)

LESSON III *DISCRIMINATION*

[MATERIALS]   Mr. Frog, the seashell, Tommy Teakettle, and pictures.

ACTIVITIES

Today we are going to have a contest. Mr. Frog invited Tommy Teakettle to visit us. We have all kinds of pictures we are going to give to Mr. Frog, Tommy Teakettle, and the seashell. Who would like to be Mr. Frog, or Tommy, or the seashell?

One of you will take a picture from the Sound Box, show it to us, and give it to one of the three—Mr. Frog, Tommy, or to the seashell. Which pictures will go to each one? (**All those with *s* to Tommy, with *sh* to the seashell, and the others to Mr. Frog.**) Who would like to be first? Tell us the name of the picture and to whom you will give it. Now you can choose the next boy or girl. (**Have the child who is pretending to be Mr. Frog hold him. Follow the same procedure for the teakettle and the seashell.**)

THOSE FOR TOMMY	THOSE FOR THE SEASHELL	THOSE FOR MR. FROG
pencil-2	shirt-19	lake-36
horse-3	washing machine-20	plumber-44
spoon-4	ship-22	flowers-45
house-6	polish-24	chickens-136
motorcycle-8	shoes-25	teacher-137
swing-10	parachute-26	cherries-144
wastebasket-17	pencil sharpener-27	top
sled-18	sugar-55	
	fish-71	
	shaving-108	

(When a child gives his picture to the wrong person, ask him to say the name again, listening for the *sh* sound and then the *s* sound.)

Our three helpers will return the pictures to the Sound Box.

LESSON IV *PRODUCTION*

[MATERIALS]   Pictures and a toy washer or a box.

REVIEW

Do you remember what things we gave to the seashell yesterday? All of them had what sound in their names?

ACTIVITIES

(Show the children a "magic" box if you don't have a toy washer. The bottom of the box is called the washer; the lid a dryer. The children take turns drawing from the washer pictures of clothing and household goods. The children ask in unison, "What did you wash today?" The child replies, "I washed [*name of article*]." The process is repeated until each child has an opportunity to participate.) Pictures used are:

suit-1	bathrobe
sweater-10	blouse
skirt-10	cap
socks-10	curtains
shirt-19	jeans
pillows-32	mittens
gloves-39	rug
coat-58	sheets
washcloth-116	shorts
raincoat-124	slip
apron-132	tablecloth
dress-135	towel
pajamas-149	

(If a child makes an error on the word, the teacher should help him by showing him how to make the *sh* sound again. Have him try the word in this way: *wa-sh*, then *wash*. If he fails after three trials, don't attempt further correction at that time.)

LESSON V *SHOW AND TELL*

(Have the children use the carrier phrase, "I'll show you my _____ _____ today.")

[ADDITIONAL ACTIVITIES FOR THIS UNIT]
1. Stories about shells, how they develop, of what they are made.
2. An artificial water flower wonder shell (costs 10¢ at the dime store) provides a wonderful surprise from two shells.

l Sound–Telephone

LESSON I *IDENTIFICATION*

[MATERIALS]   Mr. Frog, telephone, bell, and mirrors.

ACTIVITIES

Our new sound for this week is the sound the telephone makes when it rings—*ling-a-ling-ling*. It's the *l* sound. Let's pretend we're all telephones and make the *ling-a-ling-ling* sound. (**First use everyone, then the girls, then boys, then all together again.**)

Watch how I make the telephone sound. I raise the tip of my tongue, just as I do the fingers on my hand. Now you do the same thing with your tongue. Look in your mirrors and make the *l* sound.

What animals have names with the telephone sound? (**Little lamb, lion, wolf**)

You know, the word *girl* has the telephone sound. Do we have any girls whose names have the telephone sound? (**Lynette, Laura, Lillian, Libby, Laverne, Louise, Lucy, Lois**) What about boys' names? (**Larry, Lennie, Lloyd, Lester, Lewis, Leonard, Leo, Lynn, Lyle**) Do any of you have last names that contain the telephone sound?

What numbers have the *l* sound in them? (**Eleven, twelve**)

What colors have the *l* sound in them? (**Yellow, black**) The nursery rhyme "London Bridge" has lots of *l* sounds in it. Let's play the game together, and two of you whose names begin with *l* can be the bridge. (**Use volunteers. Have the girls go under the bridge while the boys say the rhyme, and then let the girls say it while the boys go under the bridge.**)

> London bridge is falling down,
> Falling down, falling down,
> London bridge is falling down,
> My fair lady.

LESSON II *LISTENING*

[MATERIALS]   A toy telephone. Sets of phones can be obtained from your telephone company.

REVIEW

Our sound—the telephone sound. We make it with our tongues—*l, l, l.* Our story today has many words with the telephone sound. Listen carefully, so that you can hear all the words with the *l* sound. How many of you have telephones at home? What sound does the telephone make? (*ling-a-ling*)

STORY OF THE TELEPHONE

A long time ago there was no telephone. When people wanted to talk to their friends, they couldn't dial a number, or call the operator and have her get the number. If a message was to be sent to someone in a far-away place, it had to be carried by a person. That person might have to walk many nights and days, or he might have to use the pony express, or ride a horse. It took a long time for people to find out when a little boy or little girl got sick. There was no way of calling the doctor; so parents had to go to his house or office to find him. When the farmer needed more men to help him plow his fields, he had to go after them. When mothers forgot to tell Daddy to bring home some milk, or some special groceries, she had to do without them unless she went to the store herself.

Life without telephones was very unpleasant at times, because many people lived very far away from each other. Letters took a long time too, because there were no airplanes to carry them quickly.

So for many years, scientists worked to build a telephone that could bring people's voices together. The man who finally invented the telephone was Alexander Graham Bell. The first ones were big, and when a person wanted to call a friend, he had to crank the telephone case. Then he'd hear the sound—*ling-a-ling.* (**Have the children say it.**) Now, all we have to do is dial a number, and we can talk to our friends in the next block or to grandma in a town that is many miles away. We can call all the countries in the world.

Telephones are lots of fun. Boys and girls like to use them. When Lennie wants to call his friend Larry, to ask him to play ball with him, he calls him on the phone. The phone goes—*ling-a-ling, ling-a-ling.* (**Have the children say the phrase together.**) When Lucy wants to tell Lynette she got a new dress for her birthday, she dials a number and the phone goes *ling-a-ling.* The telephone saves us many steps, and sometimes saves our lives. It can bring us messages about danger—like tornadoes, or heavy snow; and it can bring us messages about happy events—Larry is inviting us to his birthday party, Grandmother and Grandfather are coming to visit. So, we all are happy that Alexander Graham Bell invented the telephone.

Questions Based on the Story

1. Who invented the telephone?
2. How did people find out about things before the invention of the telephone?

3. Where do we find telephones today?

Who would like to make a pretend telephone call? Whom shall we call? What shall we say? (**Have two children carry on a phone call in front of the group. Have one of them dial a number, then the class will say** *ling-a-ling*. **Try this a few times. Remind them that we always say** *hello*, **and** *hello* **has our** *l* **sound in it too.**)

LESSON III   *DISCRIMINATION*

[MATERIALS]   **Crayons, pictures and a flannel board.**

REVIEW

What sound did Mr. Frog tell us about this week? The telephone sound. Let's all make it together—*l, l, l.* Let's hear the girls make it; now the boys. Now all together again.

ACTIVITIES

1. I'm going to name some things in the room for you and you tell me if they have the *l* sound in them. Raise your hand if they do, shake your head if they don't. (**Boys, girls, light, books, paper, blocks, doll, chair, window, blackboard**)

2. Here is a box of crayons. Who wants to pick out any crayons that have the *l* sound in their names. (**Black, yellow, purple**)

3. (**On the flannel board display the following pictures and ask the children whether the names of the pictures have the** *l* **sound in them.**)

THOSE WITH *l*		THOSE WITHOUT *l*
letter-28	plane-37	onion
leash-29	plate-38	window
camel-30	gloves-39	water
ladder-31	schoolroom-40	witch
pillow-32	slide-42	wood
girl-33	clown-43	washing
umbrella-33	plumber-44	
lion-34	flowers-45	
watermelon-35	yellow	
sailboat-36		

LESSON IV   *PRODUCTION*

[MATERIALS]   **Mr. Frog and a telephone.**

REVIEW

Yesterday we had pictures with a special sound in their names. What was it? (*l*, **the telephone sound**) When you hear me make the sound, raise your hand. Shake your head when I don't: *l, s, l, k, g, l, t, y, l*. Now all of you make the sound—*l*.

ACTIVITIES

1. First, we're going to say a rhyme you all know. Then we'll sing it. We'll always stretch out the *l* sound where we find one.

> Mary had a little lamb,
> Its fleece was white as snow;
> Everywhere that Mary went,
> The lamb was sure to go.

2. Now we'll do the same thing with this one.

> Little boy blue, come blow your horn,
> The sheep's in the meadow, the cow's in the corn.
> Where is the little boy blue?
> He's under the hay stack, fast asleep.

3. Let's have all the girls stand up and say "Mary Had a Little Lamb"; now the boys will do "Little Boy Blue."

4. Guessing game. (**Teacher starts, and encourages the children to make up some riddles too. The answer must have a word with the *l* sound. Encourage the children to reply in complete sentences.**)

   a. Who likes to roar? (**Lion**)
   b. What color is the sky? (**Blue**)
   c. Where do ducks swim? (**Lake**)
   d. What do rabbits like to eat? (**Lettuce**)
   e. What do we use with a hammer? (**Nails**)
   f. What do we like to put on our bread? (**Jelly**)
   g. What do we find on the seashore? (**Shells**)

5. We're going to take a trip to the lake. I'll start off by telling you one object I want to take, and then each of you add one. "I'm going to the lake, and I'll bring a loaf of bread." Now as you add to the list, you name all the things everyone else has mentioned. All the things we take should have the *l* sound in their names. (**Continue until six to eight items are listed by the children.**)

6. Mr. Frog thinks you've all done well, and we'll say goodbye to him for today.

LESSON V *SHARING TIME*

[MATERIALS]   **Mr. Frog and the telephone.**

REVIEW

All week we've been talking about the telephone sound. What sound does it make? (*ling-a-ling*) It's our *l* sound.

ACTIVITY

Mr. Frog would like to have you show him what you brought to school today. Can we start off by saying "Hello, Mr. Frog?" (**Each of the children takes a turn in telling what he brought. Encourage the children to start off by saying, "I'd like to show you my _____. I got it, etc." End the session by telling the group Mr. Frog will bring new games about a new sound the next week.**)

[ADDITIONAL ACTIVITIES FOR THIS UNIT]
1. Make tin-can telephones.
2. Play "London Bridge."
3. Use some of the stories for Unit 9 from Appendix B.

UNIT 10

f Sound—Funny Face Clown

LESSON I *IDENTIFICATION*

[MATERIALS]   **Mr. Frog, Funny Face Clown, and mirrors.**

ACTIVITIES

Mr. Frog has a new friend for you to meet today. This is a friend that you might see in a circus. He does tricks. He wears a funny suit. He makes people laugh. Can you guess who he is? Yes, he is a clown and this clown's name is Funny Face. We'll put a picture of Funny Face where everyone can see it.

We can learn what Funny Face does in the circus. Listen to this poem about him:

> Funny Face is a clown,
> Flippity-flop, up and down.
> Funny Face makes this sound
> Flippity-flop, round and round.
> Funny Face gives a hop
> Flippity-flop, time to stop.

Let's all say it together. (**The poem may be repeated several times. It may be used in a song form to the tune of "Twinkle, Twinkle, Little Star."**) See how I make the f sound. My top teeth touch my lower lip and the air sneaks out between my teeth and lip. My motor is lazy; it doesn't work. Make your top teeth touch your lower lip. Now let the air through. Look in your mirror as you say the f sound.

Can you think of an animal that makes this sound when it is mad? This is a small animal with soft fur; it has whiskers; it doesn't like dogs. Yes, it's a cat. Let's make the "mad cat" sound together.

Some numbers that we use have the "mad cat" and Funny Face sound in them. Can you think of a number that has the f sound? (**Four and five; numbers may be written on the blackboard for the children to see.**)

Funny Face's name has the f sound. How many of your names have this sound? Let's begin with the girls. (**Frances, Frieda, Florence, Faith, Flo**) What about the boys' names? (**Frank, Fred, Felix, Floyd**) Do any of you have last names that contain the Funny Face sound?

Can you remember all of the things that you have heard and seen today that have the *f* sound? (**Funny Face, "mad cat" sound, four, five, children's names, Mr. Frog**)

You will hear a story about Funny Face tomorrow.

LESSON II *LISTENING*

[MATERIALS]   Marcia Martin, *How the Clown Got His Smile*, New York, Grosset & Dunlap (Wonder Books), 1959. Pictures of fingers, elephant, a laugh (a smiling mouth), and a little girl.

REVIEW

Our sound—the Funny Face sound. We make it with our upper teeth and lower lip—*f-f-f*. What did the mad cat say? (*f-f-f-f*) Here are pictures of some of the things that are in our story today; Funny Face (**a clown face**), fingers, elephant, a laugh (**a smiling mouth**) and Fern (**little girl. Place these on a flannel board. The teacher may show appropriate pictures from the book to the children as she tells the story.**) When I signal, you can help to tell the story by making the Funny Face sound.

HOW FUNNY FACE GOT HIS SMILE[1]

There was once a clown named Funny Face, who was different from all the other clowns in the circus. Funny Face wore a puffy orange wig on his head. Funny Face had thick black eyebrows. Funny Face had bright blue spots on his cheeks. The other clowns had all these things too. But there was one thing that made Funny Face different.

All the other clowns had cherry-red lips that curled up in broad grins, and they were always chuckling or roaring with laughter. But Funny Face had lips that were painted blue, and they curved way down, almost to his chin, and he had the saddest look you ever saw. Funny Face never, never laughed. And all he ever said was "*f-f-f*."

His clothes were sad, too. Funny Face's shoes flapped out in front of him when he walked, and they were so old that one of his toes stuck right out the top.

Funny Face did tricks too, but his tricks made him even sadder. As soon as the circus began, Funny Face would walk around the ring with a huge wooden hammer. Suddenly he would stop, take a peanut out of his pocket, and put it on the post near the seats, where all the children could watch him. Holding the peanut very tightly between his fingers Funny Face would swing his huge hammer—once—twice—and down—right on his FINGERS! Wham! Funny Face would hold his fingers and pretend that he had been

---

[1] This story has been adapted from *How the Clown Got His Smile*, by Marcia Martin. Permission granted by the publishers, Grosset & Dunlap, Inc.

terribly hurt. All he would say was "*f-f-f.*" All the children would laugh, because they knew that he wasn't really hurt at all. And Funny Face did look so funny, with his sad mouth drooping lower and lower. Then he would run away just as fast as his big shoes would let him—flippity-flop, flippity-flop. Before you knew it, he had tripped and fallen head over heels. And again the children would laugh and laugh, because they knew that Funny Face was only pretending that he had tripped.

After this, the elephant would parade and Funny Face would flip-flop along after him. Suddenly the friendly elephant would turn and pick up Funny Face on its trunk. The elephant would lift the clown very high. Then suddenly he would lower his trunk and Funny Face would find himself sliding down to hit the ground with a loud thud! He would say, "*f-f-f.*"

Funny Face would sit there with his lips way down, looking very sad. But the children would laugh and laugh because they knew he was only pretending.

One day when the circus was playing in a little town, Funny Face came out with his huge hammer and his tiny peanut. People began to laugh when the hammer came down on his fingers—everyone except a little girl with pigtails. The little girl's name was Fern. She cried, "Oh, poor clown! Wasn't that too bad!"

Then Funny Face walked away and tripped over his big shoes; the people began to laugh again—all except Fern. She cried because she felt so sorry for the clown.

When Funny Face saw Fern, he did not know what to do. The children always laughed at his tricks. They thought that he was the funniest thing in the whole circus!

Funny Face tried all his old tricks and even some new ones, but Fern just cried longer and louder. Everyone was looking at her. After all, children are not supposed to cry when they come to the circus. Suddenly Funny Face stopped. He said "*f-f-f*" and motioned to everyone to stop laughing, and quickly flip-flopped out of the tent. People looked at one another in amazement. Even the man standing on his fingers turned himself right side up. Everyone waited for the sad clown. There wasn't a sound in the entire circus tent, except for the sobs of Fern.

In a minute Funny Face was back, with the collar of his big, ragged coat turned up high around his face. He ran up to Fern and stopped right in front of her. He said "*f-f-f.*" Then he picked her up in his arms and told her to turn down the collar of his coat. When she did, Funny Face and Fern looked at each other. And then they both started to laugh. They laughed so hard that everyone else began to laugh too.

Because Funny Face had rubbed off the dark blue lips that curled down almost to his chin, and he was wearing the brightest reddest lips and the biggest, broadest grin that ever a clown had worn. Instead of being the saddest-looking clown, he was the happiest-looking clown in the circus. Now he really had a "funny face."

Questions About the Story

1. What was the name of the circus clown?
2. What did he say?
3. What did he do?
4. Who was sad? Why?
5. What did Funny Face do to make Fern happy?
   We will play a game with Funny Face tomorrow.

LESSON III   *DISCRIMINATION*

[MATERIALS]   Storybook from the previous day, Mr. Frog, and pictures.

REVIEW

What sound are we talking about this week? (**Funny Face sound**) Let's hear the boys make the sound; the girls. Now let's hear you make it all together.

ACTIVITIES

1. I'm going to show you some pages from the Funny Face book. See if you can tell me some of the things you see that have the Funny Face sound. (**Use three or four pages. Things identified may be: Funny Face, fingers, children laughing, flippity-flop shoes, elephant, Fern.**)

2. Funny Face makes just one sound. What is it? (*f-f-f*) Clap when I talk like Funny Face. Keep very still when I make a sound that is not the Funny Face sound: *f-f-f, g-g-g, sh-sh-sh, ch-ch-ch, f-f-f, v-v-v, w-w-w, p-p-p, f-f-f.*

3. Mr. Frog has some pictures to show you. Let's see if we can name the things that are in the pictures. Some of the pictures have names with Funny Face sound and Funny Face wants these. I'll hold the pictures up one at a time and you may take turns naming the pictures and deciding if they have the Funny Face sound.

THOSE WITH *f*		THOSE WITHOUT *f*
fence-64	fur-72	wall-31
elephant-65	flags-73	pie
knife-66	frame-74	penny
football-67	frying pan-76	paper
office-68	freight cars-77	puppy
giraffe-69	refrigerator-78	top
fan-70	fire-79	water
goldfish-71	butterfly-80	wood

LESSON IV   *PRODUCTION*

[MATERIALS]   Mr. Frog and pictures with *f* sound from previous day.

REVIEW

How many of you can make the sound that we have been talking about this week? (*f-f-f*) Who makes this sound?

ACTIVITIES

1. Do you remember the poem about Funny Face that we learned? Let's say it together. Let's say it again.

2. You can all be clowns like Funny Face. (**Show actions indicated.**)

Funny Face is a clown Flippity-flop, up and down.	(**Take large steps pretending that you have on huge shoes**) (**Reach high with hands and arms; touch toes with finger tips**)
Funny Face makes this sound Flippity-flop round and round. Funny Face gives a hop Flippity-flop time to stop.	(**Same as above**) (**Turn around twice**) (**Hop once**) (**Same as in first verse**) (**Sit on floor or chairs**)

(**The children say and do the poem until they are familiar with the words and actions.**)

3. (**Have the children form a circle. One child is chosen to be Funny Face; he stands in the middle of the circle. The children are given *f* pictures from the previous day and hold them so that Funny Face can see them. They say the first verse of the poem as Funny Face does the actions. Funny Face then chooses a picture. He says, "Funny Face wants the _____ _____." He tells what he would do with the object in the picture. He takes the place of the child who formerly held the picture and this child becomes a new Funny Face. The game may be played until a number of children have had a chance to be Funny Face.**)

Funny Face will come to our sharing time tomorrow.

LESSON V *SHARING TIME*

REVIEW

This week we've been talking about the Funny Face sound. What sound does Funny Face make? (*f-f-f*)

ACTIVITY

Funny Face would like to have you show him what you brought to school today. (**Encourage each child to start by saying, "Funny Face, this is my _____." Then he can tell about the object.**)

RELATED ACTIVITIES FOR THIS UNIT

1. During art—have the children make a picture of Funny Face with construction paper or make his face of clay.
2. During physical education—play the Funny Face game.
3. During singing—sing the Funny Face poem-song.
4. During free time—place the Funny Face book where the children can look at it.
5. During number time—emphasize the *f* sound in *four* and *five*.
6. In the first grade—talk about the *f* sound in new reading words; discuss what the Funny Face sound looks like when we write it.
7. During story time—use some of the stories suggested for this Unit in Appendix B.

UNIT 11

Second Review Week: *g, sh, l, f*

LESSON I *IDENTIFICATION*

[MATERIALS]   Mr. Frog, Grey Goose, seashell, telephone, Funny Face Clown, and mirrors.

ACTIVITIES

1. This week Mr. Frog wants to see how well you remember some of the sounds we have talked about. He also wants to see if you remember the new friends he has brought since Christmas.

One week we met a friend who took Mother Goose people to the Green Garden. Who was that friend? (**Grey Goose**) What sound did Grey Goose make? (*g-g-g*) Do you know of any colors that have the Grey Goose sound? (**Gray, green, gold**)

When Grey Goose went away with Mr. Frog we talked about a new sound. It wasn't a very loud sound. Do you remember what we called it? Can you boys make the quiet sound? (*sh-sh-sh*) Are you wearing any clothes whose names have the quiet sound? (**Shoes, shirt**)

The quiet sound wouldn't have been happy with the next sound we talked about. It made a ringing sound. You use it to call your friends. Do you know what it is? (**The telephone sound**) What sound did the telephone make? (*ling-a-ling-ling*) Do any of your names have the *l* sound?

We had a friend from the circus too. Do you remember? (**Funny Face Clown**) What sound did Funny Face make? (*f-f-f*) Do some of our numbers have the Funny Face sound? (**Four, five. At this point distribute the mirrors.**)

2. Funny Face likes to watch himself in the mirror when he makes his sound. He thought you would like to look in a mirror to practice the sounds we are talking about this week. When Funny Face makes his sound, he puts his upper teeth on his lower lip and forces the air through. His motor is off. Pretend you are Funny Face Clown and make the Funny Face sound. Look in your mirrors. _____, can you show us again how to make the sound? Watch your neighbor make the sound and see if he makes it right. See if I can make the sound: *p-p-p, r-r-r, g-g-g, t-t-t, f-f-f*.

Who can show us how to make the Grey Goose sound? (**Select a child to demonstrate in front of the room.**) What part of our tongues did we use to make the Grey Goose sound? (**Back**)

Let's make the telephone sound now, *l-l-l*. What part of our tongues do we use to make the telephone sound? (**Front**)

Who can remember the other sound? Yes, it's *sh*, the quiet sound. Which of my speech helpers must work hard when I make the sound? (***sh-sh-sh, my lips***)

3. We'll divide into four groups and each group will have a chance to demonstrate something for us. Which group wants to waddle like the Grey Goose? Which group wants to pretend to curl up like seashells? Who will do the actions for "London Bridge" as we all sing it? (**Have the special group fall down each time the word appears in the rhyme.**) Which group wants to show us how to use the telephone? (**One dials, one winds the crank; all say** *ling-a-ling*, **all say "hello," and then "goodbye."**)

Everyone will sit down now; we'll all say *sh*.

LESSON II *DISCRIMINATION*

[MATERIALS]   Pictures.

ACTIVITIES

1. Can you remember all the friends and sounds we talked about yesterday? (*sh*, *f*, *l*, *g*, **Grey Goose, telephone sound, quiet sound, Funny Face Clown**)

Let's play a game with the sounds. I'll start a rhyme and you finish it.

> The telephone sound is *l, l, l,*
> Not like Grey Goose's _____. (**g-g-g**)
> The quiet sound is *sh, sh, sh,*
> Not like the Clown sound _____. (**f-f-f**)
> Funny Face says *f, f, f,*
> But the telephone says _____. (**l-l-l**)
> Grey Goose says noisily *g, g, g,*
> Be quiet, Grey Goose, _____. (**sh-sh-sh**)
> Tommy Teakettle says, *s, s, s,*
> Not like the quiet sound _____. (**sh-sh-sh**)
> My lips come out for *sh, sh, sh,*
> The tip of my tongue goes up for _____. (**l-l-l**)
> Teeth together for *s, s, s,*
> Teeth on lip for _____. (**f-f-f**)

2. I'm going to say some words and you tell me whose sound you hear. Listen and tell me when you hear the telephone sound. Clap your hands when you hear the telephone sound, and remember in what words you hear it.

collar	water
look	way
love	wish

Which words had the *l* sound? (**Look, love, collar**)
Now listen for the Grey Goose sound. (**Procedure same as for above.**)

dough	go
down	radio
get	rag

We heard the *g* sound in what words? (**Go, get, rag**)
Now tell me when you hear the Funny Face sound.

four	seat
same	roof
feet	side

In which of these did we hear the *f* sound? (**Four, feet, roof**)
Now clamp your Listening Ears on very tight. _____, will you make the Tommy Teakettle sound so everyone can hear it? _____, will you make the quiet sound so we can hear it?

Listen and don't let the Tommy Teakettle sound trick you. Clap only when you hear the quiet sound.

shoe	ship	washing	whistle
sick	wish	silly	

We hear the quiet sound in which words? (**Shoe, ship, wish, and washing**)
Let's look at some pictures. You can take turns naming them and then decide whose sound you hear. (**Shuffle the pictures named below.**)

sh	*f*	*l*	*g*	COMBINATIONS	
shirt-19	knife-66	ball-9	wagon-86	fish-23	(*f* and *sh*)
ship-22	fan-70	ladder-31	dog-90	polish-24	(*l* and *sh*)
parachute-26	fire-79	watermelon-35		girl-33	(*g* and *l*)
				leaf-69	(*l* and *f*)

(**When pictures containing two of the sounds are identified, a procedure similar to the following may be used.**) Which of our four sounds do you hear? Some of our words have two sounds that we are talking about this week. Which two are in the name of this picture?

Mr. Frog and his friends must say goodbye for today. You will see them again tomorrow.

LESSON III *DISCRIMINATION AND PRODUCTION*

[MATERIALS]   **Mr. Frog, Grey Goose, telephone, seashell, Funny Face Clown, and pictures.**

REVIEW

Which of you would like to say "hello" to our five visitors? "Hello, Mr. Frog, Grey Goose, Mr. Telephone, Miss Seashell, Funny Face Clown." Who will be Mr. Frog? Mr. Frog, you hold up one of the other visitors, point to one of your classmates, and he'll have to say that visitor's sound. Then, he can pick another visitor, and ask another boy or girl to say his visitor's sound. (**Continue this activity until the four have been named. If the children wish to continue for another round, let them do so.**)

ACTIVITIES

1. There are many riddles that have answers with the sounds we have been talking about.

   a. When I eat, I use a spoon, _____ and _____. (**Knife and fork**)

   b. On my feet I wear socks and _____. (**Shoes**)

   c. Red and green lights mean stop and _____. (**Go**)

   d. Some people are short; others are _____. (**Tall**)

   e. My mother talks on the _____. (**Telephone**)

   f. Some people are little; others are _____. (**Big**)

   g. Sometimes we pull; other times we _____. (**Push**)

   h. We count: one, two, three, _____, _____. (**Four, five**)

   i. I like to chew bubble _____. (**Gum**)

   j. Some people are big; others are _____. (**Small**)

   k. Sometimes we are bad; at other times we are _____. (**Good**)

2. (**Divide the class into four groups. You might have each select a leader who would pick his team, or you might use the simple device of counting one to four, with all one's forming the first group, etc. Each group will be given one of the four objects. The teacher will hold up a picture, and the group who should get it will so indicate. Then one child in the group will tell something about the picture. If he can't, another child in the group should be asked to try. The children must use the name of the picture in what they tell; otherwise, they don't get the picture. Since some pictures have two of the stressed sounds in their names, everyone must listen and the teacher will decide which group should have it.**)

g	*sh*	*f*	*l*
spaghetti-83	shoestring-16	fountain-48	letter-28
frog-84	bush-23	office-68	wall-31
kangaroo-89	shadow-37	giraffe-69	pillow-32
grapes-91	flashlight-44	fur-72	umbrella-33
glasses-94	sugar-55	frying pan-76	lion-34
grasshopper-96	shaving-108	freight car-77	lake-36
buggy-98	station-130	refrigerator-78	plate-38

LESSON IV *PRODUCTION*

[MATERIALS]   Mother Goose Nursery Rhymes book.

ACTIVITIES

1. You all know some nursery rhymes with the sounds we are talking about this week. I'll show you some pictures, give you some hints and we'll see where we can find the sounds in the nursery rhymes we know. (**Give clues or the first few words of the rhyme when the children can't say the poem by seeing the picture. It is only necessary to use one rhyme for each sound, but if the children think of more, they may be used. Use any pictures from a Mother Goose book for this activity.**)

f (picture of spider)—**Little Miss Muffet**
    (picture of girl with curly hair)—**Lady Fair**
sh (picture of shoe)—**There Was an Old Woman Who Lived in a Shoe**
    (picture of sheep)—**Baa, Baa, Black Sheep or Little BoPeep**
l (picture of little boy)—**Little Boy Blue**
    (picture of king)—**Old King Cole**
    (picture of bridge)—**London Bridge**
    (picture of kettle)—**Polly, Put the Kettle On**
g (picture of pig)—**To Market, to Market to Buy a Fat Pig, or**
                       This Little Pig Went to Market
    (picture of goose)—**Goosey, Goosey Gander**

2. Let's take a pretend trip to the farm. We can talk about people and animals we'll see there. We can meet the farmer and his family. When we talk about what we are going to see let's say, "We'll get to see the _____ on the farm," that have one of our sounds in their name. (**Two or three pictures from a farm storybook may be used to stimulate the children's conversation.**)

LESSON V *SHARING TIME*

[MATERIALS]   Mr. Frog.

ACTIVITY

We would like to have you show us what you brought to school today. Each of you will take a turn in telling what you have brought. You should say, "I'm going to share my _____ with you boys and girls and Mr. Frog."

Mr. Frog will have a new friend for you to meet next week.

RELATED ACTIVITIES FOR THIS UNIT
1. In art—talk about colors whose names have one of the four sounds. Make a farm mural with people and objects discussed on imaginary trip.
2. In physical education—act out the Funny Face poem; waddle and sound like Grey Goose. Play "London Bridge," "Mulberry Bush," etc.
3. During story time—reread a story used during the week that one of these sounds was introduced.

UNIT 12

v Sound–Valentine

LESSON I *IDENTIFICATION*

(Since Valentine's Day offers an excellent opportunity for work on the *v* sound, this sound should be introduced preceding this special day.)

[MATERIALS]   Mr. Frog, valentine, and mirrors.

ACTIVITIES

Very soon we shall have a special day when we exchange cards. Can you guess what it is? The cards are shaped like hearts, and they say: "To my valentine." Mr. Frog has brought us a valentine today. Can you guess what our new sound is? Valentine and Virginia start alike, and that's our sound–*v*.

See if we can make it. We put our upper front teeth over our lower lip (**demonstrate**), use our voices, and say *v* - - -. Look in our mirrors.

Do any of your names start with this sound? (**Vincent, Vivian, Van, Valerie, Vera**) Do you find the valentine sound in other parts of some of your names? (**Sylvia, Laverne, Evelyn, Eva, Vivian [2 *v*'s], Kevin, Irving, Harvey, David, Everett, Alvin, Calvin**)

What numbers do you know that have the *v* sound in them? (**7, 11, 12**) What month comes between September and Christmas that has a *v* sound in its name? (**November**)

What do we eat that is so good for us and has the *v* in its name? (**Vegetables**) On what does Mother cook the vegetables? (**Stove**)

When we make this sound we use our teeth, our lips, and what else? (**Voice**)

Does anyone know what sound we've learned that is made just like *v*, but without the voice? (*f*)

You can be Indian braves. What does the Indian say as he claps his hand over his mouth like this? (*v-v-v-v*) Get into a circle now, and when I say I am a heap big Indian brave, you say: "*v-v-v-v-v-v-v*." (**You can ask one child to be the brave, have him stand in the middle of the circle and say, "I am a heap big Indian brave." He can then tap another child to be the Indian.**)

LESSON II *LISTENING*

[MATERIALS]   **Mr. Frog, a valentine, Diva the Fly, and pictures of a boy and a girl.**

REVIEW

Mr. Frog is back with us again today. Mr. Frog wants to tell a story about Diva the Fly and a valentine party and he wants you to do two things: (1) say the valentine sound *v-v-v* when he claps his hands together, and (2) listen carefully for the words in the story that have the *v* sound.

DIVA AND THE VALENTINE

One day Diva the Fly was very restless. She wasn't happy hanging from the ceiling high above the floor. She wasn't happy zooming around the room making her *vvvv* sound. She wasn't happy diving and landing like an airplane. She just wasn't very happy at all.

Diva knew that there was something she was supposed to do, but she couldn't remember what it was!

Diva started humming. She hummed "*vvvv*" into the living room. My, but those were pretty flowers in the vase on the television set. The flowers were purple. They were violets. Diva wondered what kept the violets from wilting, so she decided to investigate. "*Vvvv*" she dived down right between the two of the violets using their stems as guides. "*V, v, v,*" Diva's sound was almost a cough. The violets were in a vase that was filled with water, and Diva had flown head first into the water. "*Vvvv*" the fly flew very quickly back out of the vase, up through the violets, and to the ceiling. Diva decided she'd better rest for a minute.

What was she supposed to remember to do? Diva thought very hard. "I believe that I should look outdoors," she thought suddenly. So "*vvvv*," away she went through the door. She was humming along so fast that she practically bombed right into a green leaf that was a part of the vine growing beside the porch. Diva settled on the vine and looked around.

Across the street a family was packing suitcases and children into a station wagon. They were going on a vacation. "*Vvvvv*" hummed the little green fly. So the neighbors were going on a vacation!

As Diva hummed in the fresh air, she flew over the mailbox. "*Vvvv*" hummed Diva excitedly. For suddenly she had remembered what it was that she was supposed to remember. Diva flew down into the mailbox and there it was! All she was supposed to remember was to get her mail today. And in the mailbox the fly found what she had really wanted all the time. Do you know what it was? A valentine for Diva! She was so happy to get a valentine in the mail that she could hardly wait to show it to all of her friends. So she pulled the valentine from the mailbox and zoomed back to the house.

Diva flew into the living room. "Look," she said to the TV set. "See what David sent me, a beautiful valentine."

"Oh, that's nice, Diva," replied Miss Vase, but she really didn't seem very happy. And the TV set just sat there staring and didn't say a word.

Diva thought perhaps she should leave the vase and TV set alone so she said goodbye and flew out to the kitchen. An olive was rolling around on the cabinet. "Look, Mr. Olive," said Diva, "at the valentine David sent me." But Mr. Olive had nothing to say. He just sat there and looked more sour than ever.

The little green fly was beginning to feel very sad because she was so proud of her valentine; yet no one else seemed to like it. Surely someone would think it was as pretty as she did. Diva flew to the dining room. A drawer containing silverware was open, so "*vvv*" in went Diva to find the knives. They would like her valentine.

"Cousin David sent me this valentine today," she began. But the knives just glanced at it and then turned the other direction. Diva moved quickly out of the drawer where the knives were kept. She was feeling worse all the time. The little green fly slowly moved toward the kitchen. She settled on top of the stove, put the valentine in front of her and sat staring at it.

Suddenly a grumbly voice said, "What have you got there, Diva?" Diva was so startled that it took her a minute to realize that it was the stove's grumbly voice. Mr. Stove would like her valentine!

"Look at the valentine Cousin David sent me," she burst out excitedly.

"Yes, it is very nice," said Mr. Stove seriously.

Diva couldn't stand it any longer. "Mr. Stove," she cried, "why doesn't anyone like my valentine? Mr. TV set and Miss Vase didn't, Mr. Olive didn't, the knives didn't. And now you act as if you don't like it."

Mr. Stove smiled a little. Then he said, "You see, Diva, each year we hear Virginia talk of her valentines and her valentine parties. And this year you have a valentine too. But Miss Vase and Mr. TV, Mr. Olive, and the knives and I stay here year after year. We never have a valentine nor go to a valentine party."

"Oh, I didn't think of that," said Diva. "Thank you, Mr. Stove. Please excuse me. I have some work to do." And Diva flew away so quickly that she forgot to take her valentine. You see, she had to find her friend, Virginia.

Virginia was just coming up the driveway. Diva went "*vvvv*" around her so fast that she practically had to shoo her away. But then she realized what Diva was trying to tell her. Night came and everyone went to bed.

The next morning was a very busy time at Virginia's house. Virginia's mother was baking cookies. "Virginia, come fix the stove so that we can bake cookies," Mother called. And a little later she said, "As soon as the cookies cool, we need to put icing on them. Bring some knives from the dining room and you can help me, Virginia. Then we'll make sandwiches with olives on them."

By the time afternoon came, it was easy to see that Virginia was going to have a party. There was a knock at the door and here came some boys and girls. Then a car drove in the driveway; it was Virginia's cousin, David.

All the children sat down at the table. They were very happy that Virginia had decided to have a Valentine Party. In the middle of the table sat Miss Vase full of violets. The children ate vanilla ice cream and the olive sandwiches and valentine cookies Virginia had made that morning. After eating they watched TV.

Miss Vase was very happy because she was in the very center of the party. Mr. Olive was happy because he had helped with the sandwiches. Mr. Stove was happy because he had baked the cookies. And the knives were happy because they had iced the valentine cookies. And Mr. TV was happy because the children watched him.

But Diva the Fly was happiest of all. She had a beautiful valentine from David. And even better than that, she had helped Miss Vase, Mr. Olive, the knives, Mr. TV and Mr. Stove have a Happy Valentine's Day.

Questions About the Story

1. What was Diva trying to remember?
2. What happened when she tried to find out why the violets didn't wilt?
3. Who didn't like her valentine?
4. Who was invited to Virginia's valentine party?
5. What had each one done to make the party a success?

LESSON III *DISCRIMINATION*

[MATERIALS]   Mr. Frog, Diva the Fly, and five valentines.

ACTIVITIES

1. All of you have heard the rhyme I'm going to tell you, but I'll go through it once, so that you'll know when to join in with the word *valentine* or *valentines.* (**Place five valentines on the flannel board, and remove them as you say the poem.**)

> Five little valentines, all in a row—
> One valentine left, and then there were four.
> Four little valentines, look—you can see—
> One valentine left, and then there were three.
> Three little valentines looking at you—
> One valentine left, and then there were two.
> Two little valentines, started to run—
> One valentine ran, and then there was one.
> One little valentine sitting all alone
> Said, "Guess I'll go in the Sound Box—
> Looks like I'm done."

2. (**Distribute the following cards to the children, and as each child shows the card to the class, have him use the phrase, "I have a _____ _____. It belongs to _____." Diva the Fly will get those with a *v* sound and Mr. Frog will get all the others.**)

v SOUND — VALENTINE

THOSE WITH v		THOSE WITHOUT v	
river-153	violin-160	ball-9	bell
valentine-154	TV-161	boat-36	bird
clover-155	gloves-162	bear-92	book
five-156	vine	bath-104	boy
vase-157	vest	bed	robe
moving van-158	stove		
vegetables-159			

LESSON IV *PRODUCTION*

[MATERIALS]   Pictures.

ACTIVITIES

1. Have any of you ever played the game in which you guess what is hanging over your head? Everyone says: "Heavy, heavy, what hangs over?" The person with something over his head says, "I have a _____ over my head." (**If any of the children know this game, let them tell the rules of the game, rather than your telling them.**)

We'll use the pictures we had yesterday. I'll start the game, and then I'll pick someone else to hold the pictures. (**Have a volunteer stand in the front of the room. All the rest of the children say the key sentence. Use the pictures in groups of three or four so that the child who must guess will be able to do so without too many failures. When he guesses correctly, then he can choose his replacement. Ask the children to stress the v sound in "heavy, heavy, what hangs over?"**)

GROUP I	GROUP II	GROUP III	GROUP IV
clover-155	bath-104	ball-9	vegetables-159
vase-157	river-153	violin-160	bear
vine	boy	bell	stove
		book	boat

2. (**Discuss with the children the meaning of the words, *cave* and *password*. Then repeat the following poem. Tell the children to listen closely, so that they'll be able to answer some questions about the poem, and then be able to act it out.**)

> We'll dig some secret hiding caves,
> For Indian chiefs and Indian braves.
> Some Cowboys, too, can come inside
> 'Twill be our favorite place to hide.
> There we'll store our Indian things,
> Like feathers, drums and magic rings.
> We'll have a pow-wow each night at seven,
> The password is "five, five, eleven."[1]

---

[1] Adapted from *My Speech Book*, Public Schools, Kansas City, Missouri, 1952.

Questions Based on the Poem

1. What will we dig?
2. Who can go there?
3. What time will the pow-wow be?
4. What is the password?

   3. (Have the children dramatize the poem. Some can be Indians and cowboys. Others can represent the feathers, drums, and magic rings.)

LESSON V *SHOW AND TELL*

Perhaps Diva the Fly will want to hear us use her sound before we start. (*v-v-v*) As you show what you have brought, tell us, "I have ＿＿＿＿＿＿ to show Diva the Fly and Mr. Frog."

ADDITIONAL ACTIVITIES FOR THIS UNIT
1. In art—have the children make valentines.
2. In number work—use numbers with *v* in them.

ch Sound–Choo Choo Train

LESSON I *IDENTIFICATION*

[MATERIALS]   **Mr. Frog, Choo Choo the Train, mirrors, and a picture of a boy chopping a tree.**

ACTIVITIES

Mr. Frog has brought us a new friend. Do you think we can guess who he is? We could ride in this friend. We could see the smoke this friend makes. This friend runs on a track. Can you guess who he is? Yes, our new friend is a train and I'll put him out where you can see him. Do you know what sound the train makes? (*ch-ch-ch*) Let's make the train sound all together. We make this sound by having our tongues touch our roofs just a little bit. Teeth are almost together. When we start the steam through, our tongues move down from our roofs. Our motors do not work. Look in our mirrors as we make the sound. Let's hear the boys make the sound. Now it's the girls' turn.

What do you suppose is the name of this train? It's Choo Choo the Train. Here is a poem about Choo Choo.

THE TRAIN[2]

> Listen to the choo choo train,
>   "ch, ch, ch-ch-ch,"
> Go down the track and back again,
>   "ch, ch, ch-ch-ch,"
> Sometimes fast, sometimes slow,
>   "ch, ch, ch-ch-ch,"
> It takes you where you want to go,
>   "ch, ch, ch-ch-ch,"
> Now it's chugging up a hill!
>   "CH, CH, CH–CH–CH!"
> Now it's stopping, Whoa Bill,
>   "ch, ch, ch-ch-ch,"
>   "ch, ch, ch-ch-ch," (**Softer**)
>   "ch, ch, ch-ch-ch." (**Softer still**)

---

[2] "The Train" by Conrad Wedberg from *Speech Improvement Through Choral Speaking* by Keppie, Wedberg and Keslar. Reprinted by permission of Expression Company, Magnolia, Mass.

Do you suppose that we could act out the train poem? Listen while I say it again and see if you can think of some ways we could be the train. (**Work out dramatization based on children's suggestions.**)

There are many times when we hear Choo Choo's sound. What sound do you make when you sneeze? That right, *kerchoo*. Let's all act as if we are sneezing. Did you hear any special sound when you sneezed? Yes, the *ch* sound. Now, let's make some sounds the birds make. (**Have several children make bird sounds. If no one suggests it, teacher may suggest "Chee, chee, chee."**) Is there anything special about that bird sound? Yes, it has the *ch* sound. Look at this picture and see if you can tell me about it. (**Picture of boy chopping down the tree.**) What sound does the ax make? Yes, chop, chop, chop, chop. We hear that sound many times.

What was that sound the train made? (**ch-ch-ch**) Tomorrow we'll hear a story about Choo Choo the Train.

LESSON II *LISTENING*

What does Choo Choo the Train say? (**ch-ch-ch**) You can help to tell the story by making Choo Choo's sound when I signal to you like this.

ACTIVITY

Read Charlotte Steiner, *The Little Train That Saved the Day*, New York, Grosset & Dunlap (Wonder Books), 1947.

(**Show the pictures in the book while reading the story. Substitute "Choo Choo the Train" for "the little freight train." Children substitute "ch-ch-ch" for "chug, chug, chug." Make the following additions: after "But the big train did not reply," insert "Choo Choo went *ch, ch* on its way." After "Slowly it started on its way back to the city," signal for the *ch* sound.**)

Tomorrow we'll play a game with Choo Choo the Train.

LESSON III *DISCRIMINATION*

[MATERIALS]   **Mr. Frog, Choo Choo the Train, and pictures.**

ACTIVITIES

1. With what sound is Mr. Frog helping us this week? Who can make it? (**Call on different individuals, then the group.**)

2. Can you tell me when I sound like Choo Choo the Train? Raise your hand when I sound like Choo Choo. Listen closely because I may try to trick you: *ch-ch-ch, d-d-d, ch-ch-ch, sh-sh-sh, p-p-p, ch-ch-ch.*

3. (**Each child should be given an opportunity to take a picture from the boxcar that stands all by itself at the train station. Some of the pictures will**

have the names with the *ch* sound and others will not. As each child takes a picture, he will say, "I chose a _____. It [has, hasn't] the *ch* sound in its name." Those that do will be placed in one of the cars of Choo Choo the Train, ready to go on to the next town. If it hasn't, it will be placed in a car on the siding that must wait for an engine. Following is the list of pictures to be used.)

THOSE WITH *ch*		THOSE WITHOUT *ch*	
chickens-136	ostrich-141	house-6	frog-84
teacher-137	punching bag-142	soap-7	gum-88
chair-137	pitcher-143	policeman-8	goose-96
cheese-138	cherries-144	socks-10	teeth-102
lunch-139	watch	shirt-19	boots-124
peach-139	matches	shoes-25	circus-125
butcher-140		fish-71	

(If a child places his picture in the wrong pile, ask another child to name the picture, and determine whether it has the train sound in it.

When all of the *ch* pictures have been placed on Choo Choo the Train, show them one at a time so that the children may name the things that Choo Choo is taking to another town.)

LESSON IV *PRODUCTION*

[MATERIALS]   Choo Choo the Train, and pictures from previous day.

REVIEW

What is the sound that we are talking about this week? Can you see something in the room that makes the sound?

ACTIVITIES

1. (Teach the children the following poem, telling them they can use it in playing a game with Choo Choo.)

> Choose, choose, Choo Choo Train today
> As you chug along your way.

2. (Have the children form a circle. One is chosen to be Choo Choo. Other children walk clockwise, repeating the poem. Each child has a picture that was used the previous day. At the end of the poem, Choo Choo says, "I choose some _____ for my train." He takes the picture of the object named and takes his place on the outside of the circle. The child who formerly held the picture becomes the new Choo Choo. Play the game this way several times.)

3. (Two chairs are used as the station in the middle of the circle. Each child takes his turn saying *ch-ch-ch* on the way to the station, where he de-

posits his load [his picture] in the right place, and *ch-ch-ch* on out to the circle.)

LESSON V *SHARING TIME*

(Each child is to bring one object that he would like to take with him on a train trip. When he tells the group about his object, have him use the phrase, "I chose a _____ to take on my train trip." Then he can tell something about it. For the children who forgot to bring their objects, have them tell the group, "I would choose to take my _____." They can tell about it.)

[ADDITIONAL ACTIVITIES FOR THIS UNIT]
1. In art work—draw the Choo Choo Train.
2. In physical education—form a train and play Follow the Leader, making the *ch* sound. Have the children think of ways they can vary the train games suggested.
3. Visit imaginary toy stores and let the children choose what they would buy.
4. Make a health train.
5. In kindergarten—build a train out of large blocks.
6. Records to play—*The Little Engine that Could* and *Train to the Zoo*, Children's Record Guild.
7. Fingerplay—play Little Charlie Chipmunk.
8. Plan a unit on transportation.

UNIT 14

j Sound–Jack-in-the-Box

LESSON I *IDENTIFICATION*

[MATERIALS]   **Mr. Frog and Jack-in-the-Box.**

ACTIVITIES

Mr. Frog wants to tell us about a new sound today—the one he calls his Jack-in-the-Box sound. Let's see if you can be jacks-in-the-box and as you jump up from your chairs, say our new sound *"j-j-j."*

We have lots of boys whose names have this sound. Let's have all those with the *j* sound in their names stand up. (**Joe, Jack, John, Jim, Jerry, George**) How many girls have *j* in their names? (**Jane, June, Judy, Jacquie, Joan, Janet, Joyce, Julia, Marjorie, Georgia**) All the boys and girls with names with the Jack-in-the-Box sound come up and play the jumping jack. (**All squat, and as the rest of the class says *j*, they jump up.**)

Do we have any colors which use the *j* sound in their names? (**Orange**)

What month is this? Does it have the Jack-in-the-Box sound? Did last month use the *j* sound in its name? Can you think of the names of other months with this sound? (**January, June, July**)

Everyone squat in front of their chairs, and when I say *j* you all jump.

All of you know the story of Jack and Jill. The names have the *j* sound in them too. Listen while I tell you the rhyme; then we'll say it together.

> Jack and Jill went up the hill,
> To fetch a pail of water.
> Jack fell down and broke his crown,
> And Jill came tumbling after.

(**Use the fingerplay, Two little birds sat on a hill.**)

LESSON II *LISTENING*

[MATERIALS]   **Jack-in-the-Box.**

ACTIVITIES

1. Welcome Jack-in-the-Box by saying the following rhyme:

> Jack-in-the-Box sits so still.
> Won't you come out?
> Yes, I will.

2. Today's story is about another Jack, Jack and the Beanstalk.

JACK AND THE BEANSTALK

A long time ago a boy lived with his mother in a little cottage. His name was Jack. His daddy had died when Jack was little; and Jack's mother struggled to get enough food for her and her son. For a while they had milk from their only cow, and at times they had jam and jelly when Jack could sell some milk.

After a while though the cow went dry, and the only way Jack's mother could provide food was to sell their last possession—their cow. She said to Jack: "You must take our cow to market and sell it, so that we can buy bread to eat."

Now Jack was a jolly boy who enjoyed talking to everyone. He put on his jacket and started for the village, with the cow by his side. As he skipped and hopped along the way, he saw an old man, to whom he stopped to talk. The man said: "You look like a bright boy. How many beans are five?" Jack replied: "Two in each hand and one in my mouth." "I see you know how to count, you will travel far. Where are you going now?"

Jack said, "I'm going to the village to sell my cow for food." The old man replied, "I will exchange these five magic beans for your cow; and if you aren't satisfied, I'll return your cow to you. These beans will become giant bean stalks, and you will never have to worry if you exchange them for your cow."

Jack jumped with joy; he put the beans in his pocket, and turned over his cow to the gentleman. When he got home, his mother said, "My, you weren't gone very long. Did you get a lot of money for our cow?" Jack said, "Oh yes, mother." "How much?" she asked. "Twenty dollars? Thirty dollars?" When Jack showed her his magic beans, she was so angry that she threw the beans out the door, and sent Jack to bed without any supper.

The next morning when Jack awoke, he found that no light was coming through his window. He jumped out of bed and ran to the window. There before his eyes he saw a giant beanstalk that had grown from the seeds his mother had thrown away. He climbed out the window and scrambled up to the very top! There he saw a house a little way off. He had climbed so high and so fast that he was out of breath. He had forgotten to eat any breakfast; so he hurried to the house to ask for food. When the lady opened the door, he said, "I'm so hungry. Won't you give me some breakfast?" She said, "You'll be my husband's breakfast if he finds you here." "Oh, please, I'm just a little boy and I only want some bread and jelly," he said. She felt so sorry for this dejected boy that she brought him into the kitchen and got him some breakfast. While he was eating, he felt the whole house shake. The lady pushed him into the oven just as a huge ogre strode into the house. Around his belt were ten pigeons which he threw on the table and said, "Fix these quickly for me for a snack while I finish that basket of cabbage. But I smell a little boy—where is he hiding?" He pounded his fists and yelled, "I'll eat him first." His wife said, "Calm down, you smell the bones of the boy you ate last night. I'm using his bones for the porridge you will have for lunch."

The ogre was satisfied with her answer. He ate and ate, and finally fell asleep. His snoring was loud and frightening, but Jack jumped out of the oven, snatched up a bag of gold that was lying beside the ogre, and ran to the giant beanstalk. He slid down the beanstalk, and to make himself light dropped the bag of gold, which landed in his mother's flower bed. She was overjoyed at their good fortune; and she even let Jack have some gingerbread cookies for his lunch.

After a while, the gold pieces were almost gone; and Jack decided to visit the house of the ogre again. He climbed out his window and up the giant beanstalk. He got to the top, and set out for the dwelling of the dangerous ogre. The lady listened to his plea for bread and jam; and again shoved him into the stove when the shaking house heralded the approach of the ogre. He strode into the kitchen, throwing on the floor ten oxen he wanted for his lunch. He jerked his head when he yelled, "There's a boy in the stove." And his wife said, "Of course there is. I'm fixing him for your dinner." Jack shivered in his cage.

After the ogre finished his oxen, he called for his magic hen. "Lay me a golden egg," he said. And behold, the hen produced a golden egg. After a while, the ogre got tired of getting golden eggs and fell asleep. Jack jumped out of the stove, grabbed the magic hen, and ran to the giant beanstalk. In a jiffy he was back at his mother's cottage, and the future was certainly bright. Never again would he and his mother have to worry about food and money.

Jack and his mother could have lived happily ever after; but Jack was an energetic boy. June came and went, and then July, and he grew restless. He decided to climb the giant beanstalk once again. He knew he couldn't ask for breakfast again, because the ogre's wife would probably recognize him. So, he hid behind the rose bushes as he looked in the window. He saw the ogre listening to a magic harp which was giving forth beautiful music. Jack was so delighted that he reached through the window, grabbed the harp, and ran as fast as his legs would carry him. The enraged ogre took after him, and poor Jack found the ogre's legs just above his head as he slid down the giant beanstalk. He called to his mother, "Bring the axe; bring the hatchet." He jumped to the ground, grabbed the hatchet, and cut down the giant beanstalk. The ogre fell to the ground, and was fatally injured.

So ended the ogre and the beanstalk; but Jack and his mother lived happily ever after with their golden eggs and golden music.

Questions Based on the Story

1. Why did Jack go to the village?
2. What did he exchange for the cow?
3. What things did he bring back from the home of the ogre?
4. What did the dangerous ogre eat when he was hungry?
5. What happened to the ogre?

LESSON III *DISCRIMINATION*

[MATERIALS]   Mr. Frog, Jack-in-the-Box, and pictures.

REVIEW

(**Our sound is Jack-in-the-Box sound. Have the children name people in the room with the *j* sound such as Jennifer, Joe, Johnny, Bridget and Fidget.**)

ACTIVITIES

1. This sound is very much like the one we learned about last week—the Choo Choo the Train sound. We all made the sound *ch-ch-ch*, and we didn't use any voice. Our sound this week is just like *ch-ch-ch*, but we add our voices—*j-j-j*. Let's make the *ch* sound, then the *j* sound together. (**Call a different child to tell you when you have made the *ch*, the train sound, or *j*, the Jack-in-the-Box sound.**)

2. Mr. Frog left a lot of pictures in the Sound Box. Mr. Frog wants each of you to *take* a picture from the Box, *look* at it, don't say anything to anyone, and *decide* whether its name has the *j* sound. If it does, you stand on the right of Jack-in-the-Box; if it doesn't, you stand on the left of Jack-in-the-Box. Before we start our game, we'll go over the pictures, so that everyone will know all the names. After everyone has taken a picture, each one will show his picture to the class, and give the picture's name.

THOSE WITH *j*		THOSE WITHOUT *j*	
cage-34	gingerbread man-152	spoon-4	doll-98
giraffe-69	bridge-153	candy-52	bed
Jack-o-lantern-145	badge	duck-53	dish
soldier-146	banjo	saucer-55	door
orange juice-147	cabbage	doctor-56	Indian
jewelry-148	engine	dog-90	socks
pajamas-149	jacket		
stage-150	jelly		
juggler-151	package		

LESSON IV   *PRODUCTION*

[MATERIALS]   Mr. Frog, Jack-in-the-Box, and pictures with *j* from previous day for activity.

REVIEW

Yesterday we learned about lots of words that Mr. Frog left for us. What sound did Jack-in-the Box make? Which of you have names that have his sound? Let's have you tell Mr. Frog your names. At Christmas time what verse did we all sing that started with the *j*? (**Have the class say "Jingle Bells" together.**)

ACTIVITIES

1. I want you to select the pictures that best answer the questions I'm going to ask. (**Use the pictures from the previous day.**) I'll put them on the tray (**or flannelboard, or blackboard**) and when you know the answer, raise your hands and I'll ask different ones. When you answer, say, "Jack-in-the-Box says it's _____" or "Jack-in-the-Box likes _____." (**Give them an example: "Jack-in-the-Box likes to eat jam."**)

    a. I like to eat _____. (**Jelly, gingerbread, cabbage**)
    b. I like to drink _____ (**Juice**)
    c. I like to play the _____. (**Banjo**)
    d. The policeman wears a _____. (**Badge**)
    e. When it's cold, I wear a _____. (**Jacket**)
    f. Some birds live in a _____. (**Cage**)
    g. Army men are called _____. (**Soldiers**)
    h. Girls like to wear _____. (**Jewelry**)
    i. A train needs an _____. (**Engine**)
    j. The mailman sometimes brings a _____. (**Package**)

2. Who knows what magic is? How many of you have ever seen a magician? What does he do? We can have one of you be the magician; and make some of our pictures disappear. We'll put five of them on the board. Then when the magician says *magic,* you'll close your eyes. Then he'll make one card disappear. When he says "Jack-in-the-Box," everyone opens his eyes; and then see if you can tell the magician what card disappeared. Who would like to be the magician? What will he say to have us close our eyes? (**Magic**) When do we open them? (**Jack-in-the-Box. Select any five pictures used in the previous activity for this one. Repeat the activity if there is time, but change the magician.**)

LESSON V *SHARING TIME*

REVIEW

Today we'll be saying goodbye to Jack-in-the-Box for a while. When we share, we'll start off by including him. We'll all start by addressing him, "Mr. Jack-in-the-Box, I have a _____."

ADDITIONAL ACTIVITIES FOR THIS UNIT
1. In physical education—jump rope.
2. Draw and/or color the beanstalk.
3. Encourage the children to plant some seeds.

UNIT 15

r Sound—Red Rooster

LESSON I *IDENTIFICATION*

[MATERIALS]   **Mr. Frog, Red Rooster, and mirrors.**

ACTIVITIES

Mr. Frog has brought us a new friend. This friend lives on the farm. He is a feathered friend. He crows early in the morning to wake up the people and the animals that live on the farm. Can you guess who he is? Yes, he is a rooster, Red Rooster. Do you know what sound he makes? (**r-r-r**) Red Rooster's sound is the sound for this week. First the boys can pretend they are Red Rooster and make his sound. Now the girls pretend you are Red Rooster and make his sound. It is early in the morning, time for everyone to wake up. Let's be Red Roosters all together.

Watch how the tongue makes Red Rooster's sound. He touches the roof along the sides, but he doesn't touch the middle. The tongue may curl up a little at the front. Our lips open just a little—like this. (**Demonstrate for the group.**) See how we make this sound in our mirrors.

What animals have names with the Red Rooster sound? (**Rabbit, giraffe, tiger, rhinoceros, bear**) And the bear goes, "*gr-r-r-r.*"

What about the boys' names? (**Robert, Ronnie, Ralph, Roy, Ross, Roger**) What about girls' names? (**Rita, Virginia, Catherine, Rose, Regina**) Do any of you have last names that contain the Red Rooster sound?

What colors have the *r* sound in them? (**Red, orange, purple, brown, green, silver**)

What numbers have the Red Rooster sound? (**Three, four**) What months have the *r* sound in their names? (**January, February, March, April, September, October, November, December**)

LESSON II *LISTENING*

REVIEW

Who was the friend we met yesterday? (**Red Rooster**) What sound did he make? (**r-r-r-r**) When I give the signal, you can help me to tell the story of Red Rooster by making the *r-r-r-r* sound. Listen for words that have the Red Rooster sound too.

STORY OF THE RED ROOSTER

Red Rooster was a very important person. He acted as the alarm clock on the farm. The farmer and all the farm animals were awakened by Red Rooster's crow, *r-r-r-r*. (**Have the children supply the sound each time it occurs in the story.**)

But, on Monday morning Farmer Ron did not hear Red Rooster crow. And by the time Farmer Ron awoke, he was supposed to have all his chores done! He rushed to the barn. All the animals were still asleep. They had not heard Red Rooster's crow either. Farmer Ron was very worried. How could he and the animals get their farm work done if Red Rooster did not wake them up early in the morning? Why didn't they hear Red Rooster crow? Red Rooster was in trouble.

Farmer Ron hunted and hunted. Finally he saw Red Rooster in a corner of the red barn. "Red Rooster!" Farmer Ron called. Now Red Rooster was asleep and when Farmer Ron called him, he was so startled that he awoke with an "*r-r-r-r-r-r.*" Red Rooster was surprised to have Farmer Ron wake him up because usually *he* woke Farmer Ron up. Farmer Ron told Red Rooster he must start doing his job better. Then he marched away, looking very upset.

A rabbit hopped into Farmer Ron's path. He said, "I can tell you why Red Rooster did not wake you and the animals up this morning. The other day he talked to Mr. Owl; Mr. Owl told Red Rooster how much fun it was to stay up at night; so Red Rooster decided to try it. He is going to bed so late at night that he does not wake up early in the morning. He cannot wake you up with his *r-r-r-r.*"

"Thank you, Mr. Rabbit," said Farmer Ron. And he went about his work.

At sundown Farmer Ron went to find Red Rooster. He took Red Rooster to a field where there were several trees. It was getting very dark. Why had Farmer Ron brought Red Rooster here? Soon a bird came flying over. It was Mr. Owl. "Watch him work," said Farmer Ron to Red Rooster. Red Rooster could hardly see Mr. Owl. How could he watch him work?

Farmer Ron said, "Mr. Owl flies above the field to find his food. He eats mice and bugs that bother my crops. How would you like to do that job?"

Red Rooster replied, "I couldn't do that. I can't fly like Mr. Owl. I can't see in the dark. I couldn't hunt the mice and bugs that hurt your crops. But, what can I do to help you?"

Farmer Ron smiled. "You were once a very good alarm clock. You woke me up in the morning with your *r-r-r-r-r-r.* You woke up the other animals with your *r-r-r-r-r-r.* We got up early to do our work."

"I see," said Red Rooster, "Mr. Owl sleeps in the daytime and does his work for you at night. My work for you is in the daytime. I need to sleep at night. Let's go back to the barnyard, Farmer Ron." Farmer Ron went to the house and Red Rooster went to the barnyard.

Early the next morning "*r-r-r-r-r-r*" woke up Farmer Ron. The sound *r-r-r-r* awakened the animals. Red Rooster was not in trouble any more.

He had learned that his work came early in the morning. He had stopped trying to act like a night owl and began to act like a rooster again. Red Rooster was back on the job.

Questions Based on the Story

1. Where did Red Rooster live?
2. What was Red Rooster's job?
3. Why was Red Rooster in trouble?
4. Who helped Farmer Ron find out what caused the trouble?
5. What time did Red Rooster wake up Farmer Ron and the animals?

LESSON III *DISCRIMINATION*

[MATERIALS]   **Mr. Frog, Red Rooster, and pictures.**

REVIEW

What sound did Mr. Frog tell us about this week? (**Red Rooster sound**) Let's hear the boys make the sound—now the girls. Let's make it all together.

ACTIVITIES

1. Here is a box of crayons. Who wants to pick up any crayon having the *r* sound? (**Red, orange, brown, green, silver, purple**)

2. Red Rooster will play a game with you. I'm going to hide a picture and see if _____ can find it. As he gets closer to the hiding place, I'll make the Red Rooster sound. When he finds the picture, he will give it to Red Rooster if it has an *r* in its name, or to Mr. Frog if it doesn't. Then _____ will pick another boy or girl who will try to find a picture, but this time everyone in class will make the *r* sound as the hunter gets close. (**The hunter should close his eyes while you have a class member hide the card.**)

THOSE WITH *r*		THOSE WITHOUT *r*
rabbit-118	red tractor-127	station wagon-21
parrot-119	umbrella-128	wash cloth-116
car-120	crutch-129	window
robin-121	train-130	sandwich
mirror-122	gumdrops-131	watch
fairy-123	apron-132	witch
raincoat-124	tricycle-133	wolf
parade-125	straws-134	wood
square-126	dress-135	

3. All of you are going to be robots for a while. (**Discuss this word if your children are not familiar with it.**)

Who makes the *rrrrrrrrr* sound? Yes, that is Red Rooster's sound too. Who makes the *r* sound? Yes, Red Rooster makes all these sounds. You must listen closely, for you are to stand very still if I make any sounds which are not Red Rooster sounds. Are you ready? Listen: *r, rr-rr-rr, sh-sh-sh, rrrrrrrrr, ch-ch-ch, r,* (squeak, etc. **Children may take turns telling the robots what to do by making different sounds.**)

LESSON IV *PRODUCTION*

[MATERIALS] **Mr. Frog and Red Rooster.**

REVIEW

Who can show us how to make the Red Rooster sound? (**If many of your children are using a *w* for *r*, bring out the mirrors again so that they can see how to round the lips for *w* but not for *r*.**)

ACTIVITIES

1. How does Red Rooster strut around the barnyard? We'll strut around our tables and make the sound of Red Rooster. (**Children may strut in a large circle if the teacher prefers.**)

2. Let's say a rhyme you know.

> Hickory, dickory dock
> The mouse ran up the clock
> The clock struck one; the mouse ran down
> Hickory dickory dock.

We'll say it again and stretch out the *r* sound when we find it.

3. Pretend that we are going on a trip. You may go on a train or you may go by airplane. You may take turns telling what you are going to ride on and where you will travel.

4. Guess some of the things that you will see on your trip.

a. There is a fire. What is that red truck? (**Fire engine**)

b. There is a farm. Who is working on the farm? (**Farmer**)

c. On the farm is a house. There is a building for the animals too. What is it? (**Barn**)

d. It is beginning to rain. Put the car inside. Do we put the car in the house? (**No, the garage**)

e. We are riding by a garden. Someone just pulled a long orange vegetable. What is it? (**Carrot**)

f. The floor of this train is soft. What makes it soft? (**Rug or carpet**)

g. Soon it will be time to go to the train diner. What will we eat there? (**Dinner, breakfast, supper, or some kind of food**)

5. Tomorrow you should be able to show or tell about something that you like that is red.

LESSON V *SHARING TIME*

[MATERIALS]   Mr. Frog and Red Rooster.

REVIEW

What new friend did Mr. Frog bring us this week? (**Red Rooster**) What sound does Red Rooster make? (*r-r-r-r*)

ACTIVITY

Mr. Frog and Red Rooster would like to see and hear about the things you like that are red. (**Each of the children takes his turn telling what he brought. He should say, "This is my red _____," or "The red thing that I like is _____." He should tell whether or not Red Rooster would like what he brought.**)

ADDITIONAL ACTIVITIES FOR THIS UNIT
1. During story time—read to the children or have them tell stories of *The Three Bears, Peter Rabbit,* or *Red Riding Hood.* Also, other stories are suggested in Appendix B.
2. In art—emphasize the *r* sound in the colors, red, orange, brown, purple, green and silver. Make rabbit ears.
3. In physical education—play Three Deep, having the child who is being chased be Red Rooster. When this child steps in front of a pair of children and stops, the child who is on the outside of the pair runs as the first child calls, "Run, Red Rooster, Run." You can also have different rules for Raymond the Robot game.

Third Review Week: *v, ch, j, r*

LESSON I *IDENTIFICATION*

[MATERIALS]   Diva the Fly, Jack-in-the-Box, Red Rooster, Choo Choo the Train, and mirrors.

ACTIVITIES

This week Mr. Frog wants to see how well you remember some of the sounds and friends we have been talking about. We'll have the boys be one team and the girls the other team. You may take turns answering the questions I ask. When we are through we will see who remembered best.

One of our friends had a party for us on Valentine's Day. Do you remember who it was? (**Diva the Fly**) What sound did Diva make (**v-v-v**) Do any of your names have the *v* sound? Do you know any numbers that have Diva's sound? (**Five, seven, eleven**)

Another of our friends could take you for a ride. Do you remember him? (**Choo Choo the Train**) What was Choo Choo's sound? (**ch-ch-ch**) Can you remember some of the things that made the *ch* sound? (**Boys and girls — kerchoo; bird — chee; axe — chop**) Do any of your names have the Choo Choo sound?

Another friend came out of a box. Who was he? (**Jack-in-the-Box**) What was his sound? (**j-j-j**) Do any of your names have the *j* sound? Do you know any story people whose names have the *j sound*? (**Judy [Punch and Judy], Jack and Jill, Jerry [Tom and Jerry cartoon], Jane [Dick and Jane first grade readers], Jack [and the Beanstalk]**)

There is one more friend we want to talk about today. He is the farmer's alarm clock. Who is he? (**Red Rooster**) What is the Red Rooster sound? (**r-r-r**) Do any of your names have the Red Rooster sound? What colors can you think of that have the Red Rooster sound? (**Red, orange, green, purple, brown, silver**)

Let's name all of our friends and their sounds: Diva the Fly, *v-v-v;* Choo Choo the Train, *ch-ch-ch;* Jack-in-the-Box, *j-j-j;* Red Rooster, *r-r-r.*

Red Rooster is very proud of how he looks. He likes to watch himself in the mirror when he makes his sound to be sure he doesn't make his beak too round. You can watch yourselves in the mirror while you make his sound. Don't make your lips too round. Now watch your neighbor. You can check each other to see if you are making the sound correctly. Now you can be Red Rooster. Get up and strut around your chairs while you make the Red Rooster sound.

Who can tell us how to make the Choo Choo sound? How do our lips go? (**They look like an "O."**) Are our teeth together or apart? Where does our tongue move? (**Down from the roof**) Do our motors work? (**No**) Let's form a line and be Choo Choo the Train. (**Select one child to be the engine.**) Check to see that all the cars on your train make the right sound.

Now make the sound again, but turn your motors on. What sound do we have now? (*j*, **the Jack-in-the-Box sound**) Feel your motors. Make the Jack-in-the-Box sound. Did your motor work? Feel your motors again. Make the Choo Choo sound. Did your motors work then?

Do our motors work when we make Diva's sound? (**Yes**) Look at yourself in the mirror when you make the sound. Now look at each other. What speech helpers can you see at work when you make this sound? (***v-v-v***) Yes, our upper teeth and lower lip. Let's make the sound again as we look in the mirrors. Be sure your motor is turned on.

Let's see if we can remember all our friends and the sounds they make. Diva, *v-v-v;* Choo Choo, *ch-ch-ch;* Jack-in-the-Box, *j-j-j;* Red Rooster, *r-r-r.* Say goodbye to them for today for they must go home with Mr. Frog. They'll be here to see you again tomorrow.

LESSON II *DISCRIMINATION*

[MATERIALS]   **Mr. Frog, Diva the Fly, Red Rooster, Jack-in-the-Box, Choo Choo the Train, and pictures.**

REVIEW

Can you remember all the friends and sounds that we talked about yesterday? Diva the Fly, *v-v-v;* Choo Choo the Train, *ch-ch-ch;* Jack-in-the-Box, *j-j-j;* and Red Rooster, *r-r-r.*

ACTIVITIES

1. Let's play a game with the sounds. I'll start a rhyme and you finish it.

Diva's sound is *v-v-v*
Not like Red Rooster's _____. (**r-r-r**)
Jack-in-the-Box says *j-j-j,*
Not like the train sound _____. (**ch-ch-ch**)
Choo Choo the Train says *ch-ch-ch*
While Diva the Fly sings _____. (**v-v-v**)
Red Rooster crows *r-r-r,*
While Jack-in-the-Box says _____. (**j-j-j**)
The quiet sound is *sh-sh-sh,*
Not like the train sound _____. (**ch-ch-ch**)
We hear the sounds of *d* and *y*

They're not like Jack-in-the-Box ＿＿＿＿＿＿＿. (j-j-j)
There is a sound called *w-w-w*,
But Red Rooster crows ＿＿＿＿＿＿＿. (r-r-r)
Babies may say *b-b-b*,
They can't say Diva's ＿＿＿＿＿＿＿. (v-v-v)

2. I'm going to say some words and you can tell me whose sound you hear. First you girls listen and watch and tell me when you hear the Red Rooster sound. See if they are right, boys.

red   read
wake   week
rake

(Children are to identify the sound as they hear it in a word and again in a cumulative list.)
We hear the *r* sound in red, rake, read.
Boys, tell me when you hear Diva's sound. See if they are right, girls.
(The procedure is the same as above.)

berry   button
very   violet
stove

We hear the *v* sound in very, stove, and violet. Now clamp your Listening Ears on tight. ＿＿＿＿＿＿＿, will you make the Choo Choo sound so everyone can hear it? ＿＿＿＿＿＿＿, will you make the Jack-in-the-Box sound so we can all hear it? Who can tell me the difference between the two sounds? When do we use our motors? (**For j**) When do we turn them off? (**For ch**)

Don't let me trick you now. Clap your hands when you hear the *j* (**motor**) sound. Be very quiet when you hear the *ch* sound.

joke   juice
check   rich
cheek   edge

We hear the *j* sound in joke, juice and edge. Listen to the words again and tell me when you hear Choo Choo's sound. (**Repeat list.**) We hear the *ch* sound in check, cheek, and rich.

3. Let's look at some pictures. You can take turns naming them and then decide whose sound you hear. (**Shuffle the following pictures. Talk about the pictures that have two of the sounds.**)

j	*ch*	*r*	*v*	COMBINATION
pajamas-149	chickens-136	rabbit-118	valentine-154	giraffe (*j* and *r*)-69
stage-150	peach-139	car-120	TV-161	pitcher (*ch* and *r*)-143
bridge-153	punching bag-142	raincoat-124	beehive-162	cherry (*ch* and *r*)-144
				orange (*r* and *j*)-147

Mr. Frog and his friends will say goodbye for today. You will see them again tomorrow.

LESSON III *PRODUCTION*

[MATERIALS]   Mr. Frog and his four friends, and pictures.

REVIEW

Can you remember all the sounds and friends we are talking about this week?

ACTIVITIES

1. We can play a game with these sounds. (**Divide the class into four groups. One group is the *j* sound, another the *ch*, the third *r*, and the fourth group the *v* sound. Set the chairs in a circle. The children should march quietly around the circle until they hear their sound. Then they should sit down quickly. Teacher says: "*l-l-l, t-t-t, s-s-s, r-r-r, g-g-g, f-f-f, ch-ch-ch, v-v-v, t-t-t, j-j-j.*" As they hear their sound the children sit down. The game may be played several times with the teacher mixing up and adding sounds *y-y-y, sh-sh-sh, b-b-b, w-w-w*, to those above.**)

2. Many riddles have answers with the sounds we have been talking about. You must take turns answering the riddles:

   a. What color is the juice you drink for breakfast? (**Red or orange**)
   b. When mother dresses up she wears (**gloves**) on her hands.
   c. In a car some people just ride; the person behind the wheel is called the (**driver**).
   d. To make food cold we put it in the (**refrigerator or freezer**).
   e. To make food hot we put it in the (**stove or oven**).
   f. We put flowers in a (**vase**).
   g. Mice like to eat (**cheese**).
   h. Some people are poor; others are (**rich**).
   i. To make people laugh we tell a (**joke or story**).
   j. When we go faster than a walk we are (**running**).
   k. Cowboys live on a (**ranch**).

3. We're going to have a story. You can help tell the story by naming the pictures I show you. (**Tell a story about the trip Red Rooster and Diva the Fly took on Choo Choo the Train to the city to find a Jack-in-the-Box. They find the Jack-in-the-Box in a toy store. Utilize as many of the pictures listed below as possible by working them into the story. If you have the toys, use them instead of the pictures.**)

Red Rooster	*Choo Choo*	*Jack-in-the-Box*	*Diva*
airplane-37	children-137	orange juice-147	vase-157
car-120	chair-137	jelly	stove
parade-125	lunch-139		violets

Who would like to ask a question about the story for the other boys and girls to answer? (**Let several children supply questions for the others to answer.**)

It's time to tell Mr. Frog and his friends goodbye. You will see them again tomorrow.

LESSON IV *PRODUCTION*

[MATERIALS]   **A Mother Goose Nursery Rhymes book.**

REVIEW

Can you remember all our friends and their sounds?

ACTIVITIES

1. You all know some nursery rhymes with the sounds we are talking about this week. I'll show you some pictures and give you some hints. We'll see where we can find the sounds in the nursery rhymes we know. (**Give clues or the first few words of the rhyme when the children can't say the poem by seeing the picture. Any Mother Goose book can be used. It is only necessary to use one rhyme for each sound, but if the children think of more, they may be worked into this activity.**)

   j: (**picture of children falling down**)—**Jack and Jill**
         (**picture of a candle**)—**Jack be Nimble**
         (**picture of a pig**)—**To Market, to Market**
         (**picture of porridge bowl**)—**Peas Porridge Hot**
   r: (**picture of clock**)—**Hickory, Dickory Dock**
         (**picture of rain**)—**Rain, Rain, Go Away**
         (**picture of garden**)—**Mistress Mary, Quite Contrary**
   v: (**picture of cat**)—**Pussy-cat, Pussy-cat, Where Have You Been**
         (**picture of shoe with buckle**)—**One, Two, Buckle My Shoe**

2. Everyone likes visitors. Sometimes they bring presents, or things with which you can play. Who would like Choo Choo the Train to come to see them? Red Rooster? Jack-in-the-Box? Diva the Fly? (**Try to have four groups similar in size.**) When your friend comes to visit you, think of some things you'd like to have him bring along. (**Have the children use the following carrier phrases as they take turns. You may want the members of the Red Rooster group to stand together in the front of the group as they talk; then have the members of another group take their places.**)

Red Rooster—**Please bring your** _____.
Diva—**When you visit me, please bring** _____.
Choo Choo—**I'll choose** _____.
Jack-in-the-Box—**When you visit me, we'll enjoy your** _____.

LESSON V *SHARING TIME*

[MATERIALS]   Mr. Frog and his four friends.

REVIEW

Today, boys and girls, you can take turns remembering who our friends of this week have been and what sounds we have worked on. *r, ch, v, j,* Jack-in-the-Box, Red Rooster, Choo Choo the Train, Diva the Fly.

ACTIVITY

We would like each of you to show our friends what you brought to share today. You can say, "I brought my _____ to show to Diva, Jack-in-the-Box, Choo Choo, and Red Rooster." Then you can tell about what you brought.

Mr. Frog will have a new friend for you to meet next week.

ADDITIONAL ACTIVITIES FOR THIS UNIT
1. In art—talk about colors whose names have one of the four sounds.
2. In physical education—develop actions for each of the identification objects or animals.
3. Dramatize some of the nursery rhymes.
4. During story time—reread a story used during the week that one of these sounds was introduced, or others which stress these sounds.

UNIT 17

Voiced *th* Sound

LESSON I

[MATERIALS]   **Mr. Frog, airplane, and mirrors.**

ACTIVITIES

Mr. Frog has a new surprise for you today. He has something that flies—something that carries people from one place to another. It has wings. What is it? An airplane! (**Take it out at this point.**) Shall we all pretend we are airplanes? First, let's learn what sound the airplane makes as it flies in the sky. It goes *th-th-th*. (**Stretch out each one.**) This is the sound we make by putting our tongue between our teeth, and using our voices. Watch me and listen. Let's try it—*th*. Look in your mirrors. I want to see just the tip of your tongue between your teeth. (**Check the children individually to make sure they are following your directions.**) Let's pretend we are the airplanes; we'll extend our arms as wings; and we'll fly around Mr. Frog, saying the airplane sound—*th*. Let Mr. Frog hear it.

Can you think of some words that have the *th* sound in them? What about mother? the? this and that? these and those? them and then? (**Encourage the children to add others to this list.**)

I know a poem that I think you will like. I'm going to say it the first time by myself. Then for the second time I want you to say the *th* sound when I signal you. Are you all listening?

> When it's time to go to bed,
> I hear an airplane above my head
> *th-th-th-th-th*.
> The airplane flies so far so fast,
> It's hardly here before it's past.
> *th-th-th-th-th*.

LESSON II *LISTENING*

[MATERIALS]   **An airplane.**

REVIEW

What sound did Mr. Frog introduce yesterday? (**The airplane sound—*th*·**

th-th) How did we make it? Do you remember the poem I told you yesterday? (**Go through it again.**)

FEATHER

Our story today is about a model airplane. This airplane was called Feather, because Ralph thought it was so light. Ralph and his brother Ronald built it in the summer before they went to Camp Leatherneck. The day before they left for camp they took the Feather to the big field outside the school. They warmed up the motor, and listened while it went *th - - - -*. For a while it looked as if the Feather would stay up in the air, but the two boys learned, after all their work, that really the airplane was too heavy to remain in the air. It zoomed to the ground, *th-th-th,* and crashed into the fence.

Ralph and his brother picked up the parts of their plane, to learn how much damage had been done. The motor still was purring—*th - - - - -;* and the body of the plane was only scratched. The propeller and one wing were seriously damaged. It looked as if Feather would have to stay in the garage till the two boys returned from camp. As they carried the plane back home, they listened to the purr of its engine, *th - - - - -.*

When the boys reached home, mother was just getting dinner on the table. Ralph and his brother hurried to wash their hands. When they were all seated at the table, Ralph started to tell his father about the broken wing and propeller. They talked about how they might pack Feather, and take it with them to camp. Then, in their spare time, perhaps they could fix it. Father offered to pack the motor for them, so that it would work well when they arrived at Camp Leatherneck.

The day the brothers left for Camp Leatherneck was an exciting one. It was their first vacation by themselves away from home. Mother had baked some cookies for them; father had packed the motor of the plane, and had made sure it would purr, *th - - - - -,* when it arrived at camp. The boys brought along some special tools, with the rest of the model plane. They couldn't wait to meet the boys who would be their playmates for two weeks. Mother finally waved goodbye to them as they headed for Camp Leatherneck with their father.

At camp the two boys found that they would be sharing a room with two other boys, Sam and Jack. As they unpacked their clothes and other things, they talked about the broken airplane. They brought out the motor and started it, even before they had hung up their clothes. Sam and Jack listened to its *th - - - - -* as they sat on the floor to examine the broken plane. Sam remembered how he had repaired one of his; and he agreed to help the brothers the next evening.

Morning arrived quickly at camp. The boys were up at six o'clock, made their beds, and were eating their breakfast by 6:30. This routine was strange to the boys; and so by evening, they were tired. The swimming, hiking, and chores wore them out. By nine o'clock, they climbed into their bunk beds and fell asleep. The purr of the plane *th - - - - -* had been forgotten.

By the end of the first week at Camp Leatherneck, however, they grew accustomed to early rising, and all the sports and games of the camp. Friday evening they remembered that their plane, the Feather, was still not fixed. They knew they'd have to work on it if they were to enter it in the model airplane race on Sunday. They pulled out the box with all the pieces; and began to work. First, they smoothed out the parts of the propeller that could be used, and smoothed out the rough parts of the body of the plane that had been scratched when it fell. Then they removed the broken wing, replaced it, fixed the propeller, and finally painted the entire plane. They tried out the motor, to make sure it was working. They liked to hear the *th* - - - - - sound it made—it sounded so smooth.

The next morning the four boys, the two brothers Ralph and Ron, and Sam and Jack, took the plane out to the field to try it. They warmed up the motor, *th* - - - - -, and soon they had Feather sailing through the air. It made a smooth landing on the ground on its first flight. So, they tried it again. Again the Feather went sailing *th* - - - - - and as it landed safely the boys knew it could win the race.

Sunday afternoon all the mothers and fathers of the boys at Camp Leatherneck came to visit. Ralph's mother brought another box of cookies, and Sam's mother brought some fruit. After the boys showed their mothers around the camp, they took them to the big field where the airplanes were to race. Ralph and Ronald had painted the name of their entry on the plane. Feather was all set to compete.

The boys lined up behind their planes, listened to the hum—*th* - - - - -, and when the signal was given, all the planes took off. Seven planes were in the air. They made so much noise that the boys had to shout. *Th* - - - - went the planes. Farther and farther they went. One came down, then another, and finally only two were still in the air. Feather was still flying. But soon it too landed—and only one was still going. Ralph and Ronald watched the winner continue to glide through the air—but, alas, it finally came down crashing. They knew what it was like to watch a plane crash, because theirs had done it only a week before. The crashed plane had flown the farthest, but it couldn't be called the winner because it had crashed. Ralph and Ronald brought their plane back to the starting line; and everyone congratulated them. Though their plane came down next to last, it was all in one piece, so they were given a prize. Can you guess what it was? Another model plane for them to build, with a bigger motor that could go whirring through the sky—*th* - - - - -. They hope someday to fly big planes themselves, and possibly fly to the moon. Then they'll be going so fast that only those who listen well will be able to hear the *th* of the motor as they fly through the sky.

Questions Based on the Story

1. What was the name of the camp the boys attended? (**Camp Leatherneck**)

2. What did the boys take to camp with them? (**Clothes, their airplane, cookies**)
3. Who made the cookies for them? (**Mother**)
4. What was Ralph's brother's name? (**Ronald**)
5. What had they named their plane? (**Feather**)
6. Who drove the boys to camp? (**Their father**)
7. What sound did the motor make when it was running? (***th*----**)

I want you to remember this story for tomorrow so that you can tell me about it. Also, we want to be able to make the airplane sound, and find all the words we can that use the sound in them. Who can tell me one now?

LESSON III *DISCRIMINATION*

REVIEW

What sound is the airplane sound? (***th*----**) Who remembers the name of the airplane that Ralph and Ronald built? Where did they take the plane?

ACTIVITIES

1. Motors make different kinds of sounds. Tell me by raising your hands when you hear the sound that Feather made. Shake your head if you hear a different sound. (**Use entire class for a few; then call on individual children.**)

a. *Th-s-th-f-th-t-th-sh-th.*

b. These will be harder—so listen carefully: *oth, os, eth, df, tho, so, show, tho.*

c. These will be still harder: *oso, otho, osho, ethe, efe.*

2. This time I'm going to ask you to tell me which word of a pair has the *th* sound in it.

here—there	gather—gander
brother—sister	brother—bottle
mother—daddy	either—fever
swim—bathe	closer—farther
him—them	seashore—weather
this—hiss	sneeze—breathe
that—cat	shave—bathe
when—then	smoothe—lose
say—they	liver—wither
mine—theirs	dough—though
these—fees	

(**Go back over those that were missed the first time.**)

3. For this sound we listen and watch. Tomorrow we'll see how much you have remembered.

LESSON IV *PRODUCTION*

[MATERIALS]   **Mr. Frog and airplane.**

REVIEW

Mr. Frog says our sound for the week is what? Do you remember how to make it? Do you remember some of the words in which we use it?

ACTIVITIES

1. Because this is our airplane sound we're going to take a trip to the moon. Each of us will bring something, and we'll see if we can remember all the things the other boys and girls have added to our list. If someone forgets any of the things on our list, we'll start all over again. Let's see how many strange things we want to take to the moon. I'll start the game, and you must follow the leader—you say what I say, and add something of your own. For *the* trip to *the* moon, I'll take a *leather* jacket.

2. We'll see if we can sing and act out this rhyme together. (**Use as many stanzas as you wish.**)

> This is the way we wash the clothes,
> Wash the clothes, wash the clothes.
> This is the way we wash the clothes,
> So early in the morning.

LESSON V *SHARING TIME*

REVIEW

We have several things we want to share today, and we'll share them with our airplane (**named what?**) and Mr. Frog.

ACTIVITY

When you show all of us what you brought, will you start off by saying, "This is _____," and then tell us about it.

ADDITIONAL ACTIVITIES FOR THIS UNIT
1. **Plan a unit on space and space ships.**

Voiceless *th*—Thumperina

LESSON I *IDENTIFICATION*

[MATERIALS]   Mr. Frog, a rabbit, and mirrors.

ACTIVITIES

When we put the model airplane away, Mr. Frog said he would be bringing a new visitor whose sound was very much like the airplane sound. It's made just like *th* (**voiced**), but this time we turn off our motors. It's the sound the bunny rabbit makes when his tail goes thump, thump, thump. So, Mr. Frog has brought us Thumperina. Shall we look in our mirrors and see how we make Thumperina's sound—*th*, without our voices this time? Let's listen to our new sound, *th, th, th*. What is our bunny rabbit's name?

Do we have anyone whose name has the thumperina sound in it? (**Theo, Thelma, Ruth, Judith, Dorothy, Kathy, Keith, Anthony, Arthur, Beth**)

What numbers do we know with the thumperina sound in their names? (**13, 30, 3**)

Can anyone think of a holiday that begins with Thumperina's sound? (**Thanksgiving**) What about one of the days of the week? (**Thursday**)

What parts of our body have names with the *th* sound? (**mouth, thumb, teeth, throat**)

What do we say when someone gives us something? (**Thank you**) Let's all say "thank you, Mr. Frog, for bringing Thumperina to visit us."

LESSON II *LISTENING*

[MATERIALS]   **Thumperina.**

ACTIVITY

I'm going to tell you a story about Thumperina. Each time you hear her thump with her tail, I want you to thump with your right foot, very lightly.

THUMPERINA AND THE PRINCE

This is a story of how Thumperina came to live on Thousand Island. When she was out playing one day, she thought about all the things she'd love to eat--carrots, and lettuce, and eggs, and milk. The longer she thought about these things, the hungrier she got. So, she decided to leave her house in the center of the tree, and take a path that would take her to a strange land. As she hopped along the path, her tail thumped and thumped. Soon she was going faster and faster. Both her ears were flapping in the wind as she traveled south. She passed her friend, Mr. Thrush, who said to her: "I think you must be in a hurry. Where are you going this fine Thursday morning?"

"I'm going to find something to eat, Mr. Thrush. Would you like to come along?"

"No, Thumperina, I think it's going to rain; so I'm going to stay here in my nest."

Thumperina looked up at the sky, but she thought that Mr. Thrush was imagining things. She continued to hop along, and as she went, she sang:

> Thumperina, Thumperina, hurry along.
> Find some lettuce before it's gone.

Soon the sky became dark and she felt some raindrops on her face. In a little while, she saw the lightning, and she heard the thunder. She became frightened. She ran so fast that she fell into a big hole. Nothing that she did helped her to get out. All she could do was thump, thump, thump, with her tail. She thought: "Maybe someone will hear me."

All night Thumperina had to stay in the hole, and she had thumped so hard that she couldn't thump anymore.

But up in his castle the handsome prince Thaw Thaw had heard the strange noise. He thought of everything that could make the noise, but he couldn't find it. In the morning he went out of his castle on Thousand Island, and started to look for whatever had made the strange sound. Thumperina tried to thump again, but it was so weak! Prince Thaw Thaw heard it, though, and he ran to the hole, and picked up Thumperina.

"Oh, you poor thing! You've hurt your foot. I'll take you to my castle, and bandage your foot. You won't be able to hop for a long time. But I'll find all the things you like to eat, and you can stay with me till you can hop again."

Many days went by. First it was Friday, then Saturday, and finally it was Thursday again. Prince Thaw Thaw and Thumperina became such fast friends that when the Prince invited her to stay in his castle, she said: "Thank you, I'd love to stay here on Thousand Island." And so the two lived in the castle. Thumperina was able to hop about, and she found all the carrots and lettuce she could possibly eat. She and Prince Thaw Thaw took many trips together on Thousand Island.

Some people say that they still are living happily in the castle of Prince Thaw Thaw. Once in a while boys and girls hear the thump, thump, of Thumperina's tail, and they know she is hopping about and finding all kinds of things to do with Prince Thaw Thaw on his island.

(Ask the children about the story, and ask them to recall the words that have the Thumperina sound in them.)

LESSON III *DISCRIMINATION*

[MATERIALS]   Mr. Frog, Thumperina and pictures.

REVIEW

Who can tell us the story we heard yesterday? (**Encourage the children to recall as much of the story as possible through questions if necessary. Some classes may want to act out the story.**)

Can you remember what Thumperina sang as she hopped along the path? Let's say the poem together. (**Overemphasize the *th*.**)

ACTIVITIES

1. Today we have some pictures which have Thumperina's sound in their names; and others which don't. I'm going to have each of you take a picture from our Sound Box. Don't show your picture to anyone, but decide whether its name has the Thumperina sound in it. If it does, raise your hand. Then I'll have you show it to us, tell us what it is, and you can place it in front of Thumperina. Then those who have pictures whose names don't have Thumperina's name will take turns in telling us their pictures, and then they'll give them to Mr. Frog.

THOSE WITH *th*		THOSE WITHOUT *th*	
thimble-100	birthday cake-111	suit-1	fan-70
mouth-102	thread-112	soup-4	fork-76
bathtub-105	Thanksgiving-113	house-6	refrigerator-78
booth-106	thermos-115	scrapbook-17	potato
thermometer-107	washcloth-116	turkey-53	gate
throne-109	toothbrush-117	fence-64	goat
wreath-110		football-67	

2. (**Place on a flannel board or other support sets of three pictures, and call on individual children to tell which ones have names with the *th* sound. Any grouping will do; for instance, thread, fork, soup.**)

3. (**Have the children stand in a circle, with one of them in the middle.**) Those in the circle say:

> Thimble, thimble, thimble, three
> The one I touch runs after me.

(**The child in the center then touches one of those in the circle, and the game of tag ensues.**)

LESSON IV *DISCRIMINATION AND PRODUCTION*

[MATERIALS]   A thimble.

ACTIVITIES

1. Are our Listening Ears on tight? We'll need them, because you must listen closely and watch carefully if you are to tell me if the two words I say have the Thumperina sound in them. We'll take turns in answering.

thin—fin	something—everything
win—thin	thigh—sigh
think—thing	thin—thick
anything—nothing	thirty—forty
horn—thorn	thick—sick
tooth—Ruth	few—threw
sing—thing	some—thumb
three—see	sought—thought

2. We're going to play the game of hiding the thimble. Who will be our first Thumperina? Now, you tell one of the boys or girls to close his eyes while you hide the thimble. As he looks for it, all of us will say "thump, thump" very softly as he gets close to it, and we'll get louder as he gets further away from the hiding place. When he finds the thimble, he can choose another boy or girl to close his eyes.

LESSON V *PRODUCTION*

[MATERIALS]   **Thumperina and pictures.**

ACTIVITIES

1. Today we have a poem about Thumperina which we'll learn, so that we can use it in our game. Listen while I say it; then we'll say it together.

> Thumperina, Thumperina, thumped on a log
> Thumperina, Thumperina, saw a frog.
> Thumperina played the whole day through
> I can be Thumperina, can you?

Now we'll form a circle. Who wants to be Thumperina and stand in the middle of the circle? As we say the poem, we'll tap our right foot in rhythm. Thumperina will have to help us. (**At the end of the poem, the leader points to another child who takes his place in the center of the circle. Play the game till four or five children have been Thumperina.**)

2. We're going to play a guessing game which needs another Thumperina. Thumperina will draw a card, and she'll give us clues to see if we can guess what picture she has. If she were to say, "It's something that we use when

we take a bath," what would you guess? Thumperina will call on us when we raise our hands, and whoever guesses right, becomes the new Thumperina.

PICTURES TO USE

thimble-100	thread-112
mouth-102	Thanksgiving-113
bathtub-105	thermos-115
thermometer-107	washcloth-116
birthday cake-111	toothbrush-117

LESSON VI *PRODUCTION*

REVIEW

What sound are we learning about this week? (**Thumperina sound— th, th**)

ACTIVITIES

1. First we'll have a few riddles which require answers with Thumperina's sound in them.

   a. What number comes after two?
   b. When you get dirty, what do you take?
   c. What do we call the noise in the sky when it's raining?
   d. What does Mother wear on her finger when she sews?
   e. What finger is this? (**Hold up your thumb.**)
   f. What helps us to chew our food?
   g. When someone gives you something, what do you say?
   h. What day comes after Wednesday?
   i. What does Mother put in our mouths to get our temperature when we are sick?

2. (This next activity can be expanded into a lesson which utilizes a map, or it can be one that merely stresses places that are near or far away. The children are to decide which ones want to go to the North Pole, and those who want to go to the South Pole. They can form two teams, each of which will try to think of things they would bring back from the Poles to show the class. Have the members of each team take turns in telling what they would bring back. Have them use the carrier phrase, "I'll bring _____ _____ from the South Pole." Those children who can't think of anything should tell their teammates, "I can't think of anything to bring back.")

LESSON VII *PRODUCTION*

[MATERIALS]   Thumperina, birthday cake, and pictures.

ACTIVITIES

Today our Thumperina is going to have a birthday party. (**The birthday party can be held during the milk period if you wish. As the children get their milk and cookies, encourage them to say, "Thank you, Thumperina." After the milk and cookies are eaten, have the children sing, "Happy Birthday" to Thumperina. Then in a box on which you have placed a picture of a birthday cake, have the pictures from Lesson III which the children will select. After each child has a picture, have him give it to Thumperina. If a child is making a mistake on the *th* sound, observe what he does. He may be saying *s* or *f*. Give him the correct pattern, and encourage him to imitate you as you say,** *Thumperina.*)

LESSON VIII *SHARING TIME*

Thumperina will be saying goodbye to us today for a while; so let's show her how well we remember her sound. Let's start our sharing time by saying, "I have something to show you, Thumperina."

ADDITIONAL ACTIVITIES FOR THIS UNIT
1. Read or tell the story of Tom Thumb, and any others from Appendix B, Unit 18.
2. Emphasize the numbers, such as 3, 13, 30 in the number work; possibly even fourth, fifth, etc.
3. Draw or color Thumperina, her eggs, and possibly her basket.
4. Have a unit on rabbits, their habitat, and how they live.

Review of all Sounds

LESSON I *IDENTIFICATION*

[MATERIALS]   **All the identifying objects used in previous lessons.**

When Mr. Frog opened the Sound Box today, he found that he couldn't get his fingers inside. It was so full that he wants us to help him to empty it. What could be in there? Would someone like to look inside the Sound Box? Well, certainly, all of our storybook people are back to see us! Wouldn't it be fun if we had a living storybook? Each of you can be one of our story-book people, or his helper. As I take one of the books or objects from the Sound Box, those of you who want to pretend to be it, raise your hands. (**As you remove each object, ask the children something about the story in which the object figured. Wherever possible work in a question which requires that the children say the sound in isolation. For instance, where did the Grey Goose take her family for the winter?** *How* **did Father Goose let Mother Goose know that Billy Goat could take the trip with them? Who remembers the name of the model airplane that the brothers Ralph and Ronald built?** *What* **sound did it make as it crashed?**)

Now that we have all of our storybook people selected, we must find helpers for them. (**The number of helpers will depend on the number of children in the room. We have 15 characters. As a surprise let the child who is chosen last, be Mr. Frog. Some typical combinations from the stories could be the following.**)

Captain Kangaroo and Koko
Father and Mother Goose
Buzzing Bee and Zelda
Telephone and Bell
Jack-in-the-Box and Jack and the Bean-
  stalk
Peter Pig and his brother Paul
Valentine and Diva the Fly

Thumperina and Prince Thaw Thaw
Red Rooster and Farmer Ron
Airplane, Feather, and Ralph's
  brother, Ronald
Funny Face and Fern, or the elephant
Choo Choo the Train and engine
Quiet sound and seashell
Tommy Teakettle and Sue

Mr. Frog is going to tap someone on the shoulder while all of you close your eyes. Whoever is tapped will get his partner and the two of them will come up beside Mr. Frog and tell us who they are. When they tell us what sound they made, everyone will join in. (**If a child forgets his sound or makes it incorrectly, help him or have the helper assist him.**)

LESSON II *DISCRIMINATION AND PRODUCTION*

[MATERIALS]   All the objects and some pictures and strips of paper.

ACTIVITIES

Our storybook people are ready to come out of the Sound Box. Mr. Frog, can you help me to give out the objects? Before you can have your "pretend" character though, you'll have to say the password—"Thank you, Mr. Frog." Yesterday each storybook person had a helper. Pair off again today, so that when your storybook person is to be given to you, you can say the password together.

Now that all of you have your storybook people, Mr. Frog will be giving our teams some pictures. As each team takes turns holding up a picture and telling us what it is, whoever thinks they should have it should raise their hands. For instance, if they show you the picture of a *car*, who should get it? (**Captain Kangaroo, Red Rooster, and their helpers**) So I'll give the four of you a strip of paper. At the end of our game, we'll see who has the most strips.

PICTURES TO BE USED

policeman and motorcycle-8	birthday cake-111
school-12	washcloth-116
station wagon-21	fairy-123
polish and brush-24	electric train-130
girl and umbrella-33	teacher and children-137
plumber-44	punching bag-142
truck and tractor-51	orange juice-147
squirrel-60	pajamas-149
elephant-65	valentine-154
fireplace-79	vegetables-159
kangaroo-89	zebra-169
globe-97	rose-171
weather vane-103	

Count your strips to see who are the winners. What was our password for today? As you put your storybook people in the Sound Box say the password. (**Either Mr. Frog can collect the items, or the children can bring the items to the Sound Box.**)

LESSON III *LISTENING AND PRODUCTION*

[MATERIALS]   All of the objects and the following pictures: broom, ladder-31, nests, woodpecker.

ACTIVITIES

Today I'm going to tell you about the story of spring. It's the season of the year that comes after the snow has disappeared. It begins to get warm. All kinds of things pop out of the ground, people start thinking about vacations, and Easter will come soon. As I tell the story, I'll be holding up some of our storybook people, and when I do, you'll say their names.

SPRINGTIME

Springtime in the country means that farmers get ready to plant their seeds. They look forward to big wheat crops and corn crops. They think about all the carrots and potatoes they will be able to grow on the farm. Fences too need to be repaired after the winter winds. The *pigs* may wander out into the corn fields if the fences aren't strong. *Thumperina* may hop over into the lettuce beds if she gets a chance.

Every morning *Red Rooster* awakens everyone on the farm. The *Buzzing Bee* flies out of his hive; the *Grey Goose* who has just returned from the Green Garden, flaps his wings. *Captain Kangaroo* opens his sleepy eyes, and remembers he must find bamboo shoots for his Panda, *Koko*. He sets *Tommy Teakettle* on the stove to heat some water. He wants a cup of hot tea before he begins his hunt.

Springtime in the city means that the trees are beginning to bud, flowers are peeking through the ground, and everyone is glad to put away snow shoes and heavy coats. *Valentine's* Day has come and gone, and *Jack-in-the-Box* is ready to bring surprises to everyone. He and *Funny Face* eagerly plan a trip to find new adventures.

Everywhere people are calling on the *telephone* to make plans for Easter. Some folks will take the *airplane* to visit far-away cities. The hum of the motor as it goes *th* - - - will be heard by boys and girls who watch the sky and listen. Others will get on *Choo Choo the Train* and travel more slowly to visit friends.

Springtime is also clean-up time. We get out our *brooms* to sweep away the winter's dirt. We buy fresh *paint* to brighten our houses. We climb the *ladder* to mend the roof.

Birds return from the south again. They build their *nests* in the trees, and wait for their eggs to hatch. The *woodpecker* pecks away at the trees in the shady meadow.

Everyone is happy when spring is here! (**During the telling of this story, you may want to call on individual children to name the object you display for them.**)

Tomorrow we'll be taking an imaginary trip to a far-away place. You should be thinking where you would like to go, and what your storybook people would probably want to take with them.

LESSON IV *PRODUCTION*

[MATERIALS]   **All the objects.**

ACTIVITIES

1. Today we are going to take a trip. Where shall it be? (**It could be to Walt Disney's storyland, to the land over the rainbow, to the house that Jack built, to the North Pole, etc. When the children have decided, then each will be given his storybook character, and together with his helper, will decide what they'll take with them. During this lesson stress the use of carrier phrases, such as "I'm Mr. Kangaroo, and I'll take some _____ _____ to the _____. Or, I'm Mr. Kangaroo's helper, Koko, and I'll need some _____ for my trip to the _____." Have the children pair off, as they did previously, and as they tell the group, have them stand together.**)

2. Make-believe land is fun, don't you think? Do you remember the song about wishing upon a star? Can we sing it together?

Tomorrow we'll bring our things for sharing time. Mr. Frog will expect you to talk so that he can understand what you say.

LESSON V   *SHARING TIME*

Since today will be the last time we'll have our storybook people with us, we will show our things today to all of them and when we finish, tell them "Thank you" for coming.

APPENDIXES

APPENDIX A
Suggested Materials for Each Unit

The suggested materials for each unit are given below, including the approximate cost, and sources from which they can be obtained.

ALL UNITS

Rubber frog (R 11)	42¢
Mirrors	10¢ each
Crayons	25¢
Speech Improvement Cards	$5.75
Scrap book	
Paper "ears"	
Sound box	

UNIT 1

Records:	*Let's Listen*	$3.95
	Muffin in the City	2.49
	Muffin in the Country	2.49
Filmstrips:	*Our Talking Helpers*	5.00
Noisemakers:	whistles, rattle,	
	bell	10¢–20¢ each

UNIT 2

Rubber pig (R 2), 60¢

UNIT 3

Kathleen N. Daly, *Captain Kangaroo and the Panda,* New York, Golden Press, 29¢

UNIT 4

A toy teakettle, 50¢

UNIT 5

A bee, 59¢
A purse

UNIT 6

Four Christmas stockings (if unit precedes Christmas), 39¢ each

UNIT 7

Grey Goose, 59¢

UNIT 8

Seashells, 10¢ and up

UNIT 9

Telephone, $1.00

UNIT 10

Marcia Martin, *How the Clown Got His Smile,* New York, Grosset & Dunlap (Wonder Books), 39¢

UNIT 11

A Mother Goose Nursery Rhymes book

UNIT 12

A fly, 59¢
Valentines, 5¢ and up

UNIT 13

A train, $1.00

UNIT 14

A Jack-in-the-Box, $1.00

UNIT 15

A rubber red rooster (R 39), 60¢

UNIT 16

Mother Goose Nursery Rhymes book

UNIT 17

An airplane, 10¢ and up

UNIT 18

A rubber rabbit (R 3), 36¢
Cardboard birthday cake

Rubber animals are Remple toys and can be purchased in most toy departments, or they can be ordered directly from: Remple Manufacturing Company, Inc., 100 Tubb Avenue, West Point, Mississippi. Prices quoted do not include postage.

Speech Improvement Cards, Revised, by Bryngelson-Glasby, 1963, can be ordered from: Scott-Foresman, Chicago 11, Illinois.

Filmstrip is available from: Webster Publishing Company, 1808 Washington Avenue, St. Louis 3, Missouri.

Records: The *Muffin* records are available from Children's Music Center, 5373 W. Pico Blvd., Los Angeles, California. *Let's Listen,* M. Marie Bresnahan and William L. Pronovost, Ginn and Company, New York, New York.

Other objects: Items like the goose, Jack-in-the-Box, Wonder and Golden Books, and other materials can be purchased in any local toy store.

APPENDIX B

Additional Stories for Each Unit

This list suggests types of stories that can be used, but it is by no means exhaustive.

UNIT 1

Borten, Helen, *Do You Hear What I Hear?*, New York, Abelard-Schuman Ltd., 1960.

Brown, Margaret W., *The Country Noisy Book*, New York, Harper & Row, 1940.

Kuskin, Karla, *All Sizes of Noises*, New York, Harper & Row, 1962.

UNIT 2

Newberry, Clare, *Percy, Kelly, and Pete*, New York, Harper & Row, 1952.

Potter, Beatrix, *The Tale of Peter Rabbit*, New York, Frederick Warne and Co., 1903.

UNIT 3

Bannerman, Helen, *The Story of Little Black Sambo*, Philadelphia, J. B. Lippincott Co., 1923.

Gag, Wanda, *Millions of Cats*, New York, Coward-McCann, Inc., 1928.

Payne, Emmy, *Katy-No-Pocket*, Boston, Houghton Mifflin Co., 1944.

Scott, Louise B., and J. J. Thompson, "Story of Timmy Teakettle," from *Talking Time*, St. Louis, Mo., Webster Publishing Co., 1951.

Dr. Seuss, *The Cat in the Hat*, New York, Random House, 1957.

Slobodkina, Esphyr, *Caps for Sale*, New York, William R. Scott, 1947.

Thaler, M., *The Clown's Smile*, New York, Harper & Row, 1962.

UNIT 4

Bannerman, Helen, *The Story of Little Black Sambo*, Philadelphia, J. B. Lippincott Co., 1923.

Scott, Louise B., and J. J. Thompson, "Story of Timmy Teakettle," from *Talking Time*, St. Louis, Mo., Webster Publishing Co., 1951.

UNIT 5

Baum, L. F., *Wizard of Oz*, New York, Grosset & Dunlap (Wonder Books).

Hader, Berta, *Lost in the Zoo*, New York, The Macmillan Co., 1951.

UNIT 6

Any of the Christmas stories, if this unit is scheduled as suggested during this period.

UNIT 7

Asbjournsen, P. C., and J. E. Moe, *The Three Billy Goats Gruff*, New York, Harcourt, Brace & World, Inc., 1957.

Dr. Seuss, *Green Eggs and Ham*, New York, Random House, 1960.

UNIT 8

Ayer, Jacqueline, *A Wish for Little Sister*, New York, Harcourt, Brace & World, Inc., 1960.

Jacobs, J., *The Three Wishes*, New York, Whittlesey House, 1961.

Scott, Louise B., and J. J. Thompson, "The Seashell," from *Talking Time*, St. Louis, Mo., Webster Publishing Co., 1951.

UNIT 9

Daugherty, J., *Andy and the Lion*, New York, The Viking Press, Inc., 1938.

Fatio, Louise, *The Happy Lion's Quest*, New York, Whittlesey House, 1961.

UNIT 10

Elkin, B., *Six Foolish Fishermen*, New York, Childrens Press, 1957.

UNIT 11

Dennis, Wesley, *Flip*, New York, The Viking Press, Inc., 1941.

Dennis, Wesley, *Flip and the Cow*, New York, The Viking Press, Inc., 1942.

Dennis, Wesley, *Flip and the Morning*, New York, The Viking Press, Inc., 1951.

UNIT 12

Any stories about Valentine's Day if this unit immediately precedes this holiday, as suggested.

UNIT 13

Martin, B., *Smoky Poky*, New York, Holt, Rinehart and Winston, Inc., 1947.

Miller, Olive B., ed., "The Little Engine That Could," from *The Book House for Children*, Lake Bluff, Ill., Tangley Oaks, 1951.

Slobodkina, Esphyr, *Behind the Dark Window Shade*, New York, Lothrop, Lee & Shepard Co., Inc., 1958.

UNIT 14

Friskey, Margaret, *Johnny and the Monarch*, New York, Childrens Press, 1961.

Nemoy, Elizabeth M., "Where the Jam Jars Grow," from *Speech Correction Through Story-Telling Units*, Magnolia, Mass., Expression Co., 1954.

Thayer, Jane, *The Second-Story Giraffe*, New York, William Morrow and Co., 1959.

UNIT 15

Parkin, Rex, *The Red Carpet*, New York, The Macmillan Co., 1948.

Zion, Gene, *No Roses for Harry*, New York, Harper & Row, 1958.

UNIT 18

Anderson, H., *Thumbelina*, New York, Charles Scribner's Sons, 1961.

Fatio, Louise, *The Three Happy Lions*, New York, Whittlesey House, 1959.

Scott, Louise B., and J. J. Thompson, "Thumpy," from *Talking Time*, St. Louis, Mo., Webster Publishing Co., 1951.

APPENDIX C
Additional References

A. Stories for listening time will be found in the following books:

Nemoy, Elizabeth M., and Serena F. Davis, *Correction of Defective Consonant Sounds,* Expression Co., 1937.

Nemoy, Elizabeth M., *Speech Correction Through Story-Telling Units,* Expression Co., 1954.

Scott, Louise B., and J. J. Thompson, *Talking Time,* St. Louis, Mo., Webster Publishing Co., 1951.

Zedler, Empress, *Listening for Speech Sounds,* New York, Harper & Row, 1955.

B. Music books written particularly for kindergarten and first-grade children have many excellent songs that can be selected by the teacher to stress the sounds in the program.

APPENDIX D
Alphabetical List of Pictures and Appropriate Units

BG indicates that the picture is one of the Bryngelson-Glasby cards. The numbers after the pictures indicate the Units in which the picture is utilized.

airplane   BG 2, 6, 9, 16
apron   BG 8, 15
baby   2
bacon   BG 3
badge   14
balls   BG 2, 7, 11, 12
banjo   14
basket   BG 3
bath   BG 12
bathrobe   8
bathtub   BG 18
bear   BG 2, 12
bed   2, 7, 12, 14
beehive   BG 16
bees   BG 6
bell   12
bird   2, 12
birthday cake   BG 18, 19
blouse   8
boat   BG 2, 12
book   12
booth   BG 18
boots   BG 13
boy   BG 2, 12

bridge   BG 14, 16
broom   19
brush   BG 2, 4
buggy   BG 7, 11
bunny rabbit   BG 2
bush   BG 11
butcher   BG 13
butter   2
butterfly   BG 10
cabbage   14
cage   BG 14
camel   BG 9
candy   BG 3, 6, 7, 14
cap   BG 2, 8
car   BG 15, 16
cat   BG 3, 6
chair   BG 13, 16
cheese   BG 13
cherries   BG 8, 13, 16
chickens   BG 8, 13, 16
children   BG 16
Christmas tree   BG 4
circus   BG 4, 13
clock   BG 3, 6

clover   BG 12
clown   BG 9
coat   BG 3, 6, 8
cow   BG 3
crutch   BG 15
cup   BG 2, 3
curtains   8
desk   BG 4, 7
dishes   4, 7, 14
doctor   BG 3, 14
dog   BG 7, 11, 14
doll   BG 7, 14
door   14
dress   BG 7, 8, 15
duck   BG 7, 14
easel   BG 6
eggs   BG 7
elephant   BG 3, 10, 19
engine   14
fairy   BG 15, 19
fan   BG 10, 11, 18
fence   BG 10, 18
fire   BG 2, 10, 11
fireplace   BG 19

APPENDIXES